Apes

Apes

Gorillas, chimpanzees, orangutans and gibbons
Ray Hutchins

Illustrated by Ray Hutchins

MERLIN PUBLICATIONS

First publishe   i the United Kingdom by Merlin Publications 2010.
Written anc   strated by Ray Hutchins FLS, FZSL, FCSD.

ISBN 0-95 3070-2-X

Design: R)lando Ugolini
Illustrati(1s: Ray Hutchins

First Ec ûon

Print   by Gold Printing Group Limited, China

Dedication and Acknowledgements

The references for this book rely upon the work of many experts including:

Professor Colin Groves for his great help on taxonomy and general overview.
Dr. Jane Goodall and staff of The Jane Goodall Institute for information on chimpanzees.
Ian Redmond OBE for technical checks and reference material.
Thomas Geissmann (Zurich University and Gibbon Conservation Alliance) for help with the gibbons.
Ashley Leiman OBE, Director of The Orangutan Foundation and her staff for help with photographs and advice.
Karen Payne and **Clare Campbell** of Perth Zoo, Australia, for help with gibbon and orangutan reference photographs.
Sofie Meilvang Assistant Project Manager, Limbe Wildlife Centre, Cameroon, for information and reference material on Cross River gorilla and Nigerian/Cameroon chimpanzee.
Mr. Peter Hough for moral support and **Nancy** for those cups of tea!

This book is dedicated to my loving wife, Yvonne, without whom this book would never have been written.

Contents

Foreword

This splendid book will open your eyes about apes. It tells you what they are, how many species and subspecies there are, how they differ, where and how they live, and what we, though essentially apes ourselves, are doing to them and how we are threatening their very prospects for survival (and what, in a very small way, some of us are trying to do about it to reverse this sad trend).

The text is very clearly written, and the most challenging concepts are explained so lucidly that they are easily grasped, and so interestingly that people who had no concern for apes before will start looking at them with different eyes. There are all sorts of goodies that you won't find in other books, like the explanation of their scientific names and an introduction to who described them and when and why.

But it is the artwork that really makes this book stand out in a crowd. Ray Hutchins depicts the apes accurately, and in so doing he has captured their essence. After a long period when painting and drawing were considered superfluous because colour photography had reached such a pitch of perfection, we have come once more to an appreciation that an accurate painting can show things that photography cannot, and that a skilled artist can add immeasurably to our understanding of the subject. Ray Hutchins is one of the leading exponents in this rediscovery of the beauty of the beast.

This book is going to find a place on the shelves of every school library, and very likely in every zoo bookshop, in universities -- and on your private bookshelf.

Colin Groves
Professor of Biological Anthropology
Australian National University
Canberra
Australia

The Apes
Gorillas, chimpanzees, orangutans and gibbons

There are five kinds of apes. They are the gorillas, orangutans, chimpanzees, including the bonobo, gibbons and humans (us!); but this book will show and describe only our non-human cousins.

Apes are not monkeys. For a start apes do not have tails, but the most important difference is that apes are more intelligent, have fewer young and spend a longer time raising them. Their brains are larger and more developed than monkeys and apes can learn and pass along information. Apes all have the same dental formula as humans.

The Superfamily

Apes and humans are members of the same superfamily called the Hominoidea. Until recently humans were regarded as a separate family within this superfamily because it was believed that we are much different to the apes; but, recent genetic studies and discoveries from the fossil record have made it clear that some of the apes are more similar to humans than previously believed. Subsequently, the living hominoids are now commonly classified into only two families, with humans grouped with the great apes. The two families consist of: the Hylobatidae, the gibbons, and the Hominidae, the orangutans, gorillas, chimpanzees and bonobos, and - humans - us!

It is a fact that chimpanzees are known to share more genetic material with humans, about 99%, even more than they do with gorillas.

How many are there?

Most people believe that there is just one race of each of the gorillas, chimpanzees, orangutans and gibbons, mostly because of what is considered common knowledge and what is seen on the television; but, you will find that there are more different species and subspecies to see and learn about as you read on.

Where do they live?

Gorillas, chimpanzees, and bonobos live in groups in Africa. Humans originated in Africa as well. Orangutans live in Indonesia and Malaysia and gibbons live in Indonesia, Malaysia and China.

What attracts us to them?

What makes the great apes so fascinating? Maybe it's because they remind us of ourselves. They use gestures and facial expressions that look much like ours, even though these may have a very different meaning. For example, what looks like a big smile on a chimpanzee may be a "fear grin" that means it is scared.

Similarities and differences

Like us, apes have flat fingernails and complicated fingerprints, and their hands are capable of grasping. But, unlike us, their bodies are designed to be most comfortable walking on all fours, except for the gibbons who normally walk bipedally. Apes have arms longer than their legs.

> ### Did you know? ...
>
> *The Carthaginian explorer Hanno, on an expedition to West Africa, is reputed to have found Gorillas and brought their skins to Carthage (near modern Tunisia) in 460 BC. He named them 'gorillae' from the then local African term for 'wildman'. They first appeared in scientific literature in 1847 when a Dr Thomas Savage sent skulls to the Boston Natural History Society which reported his finds; but, it was not until 1860 that the existence of Gorilla was finally proven by the Franco-American du Chaillu, who has the dubious honour of being the first white man to have shot a gorilla. Even then, on producing the skins to a sceptical scientific world, he was still not totally believed! The first live gorilla to reach Europe in the late 1800's survived for just two weeks.*

> ### The family tree
>
> | | | |
> |---|---|---|
> | Hominoidea | | superfamily |
> | Hominidae · Hylobatidae | | family |
> | Homininae · Ponginae | | subfamily |
> | Hominini · Gorillini | | tribe |
> | Homo · Pan · Gorilla · Pongo · Hylobates | | genus |
>
> *The taxonomic family tree of the Hominoids, the apes. You will see that humans are included. The gibbons are divided into four genera as the individual descriptions will show.*

Ape habitats

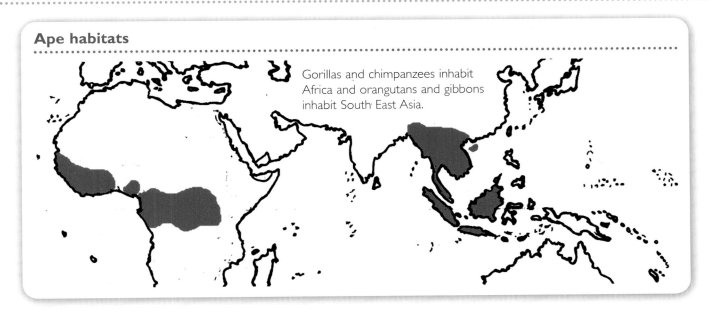

Gorillas and chimpanzees inhabit Africa and orangutans and gibbons inhabit South East Asia.

The gorillas

The largest apes are the gorillas of Africa. They are massive animals and have large heads and stout and very muscular bodies.

Like humans, gorillas are terrestrial animals. They move on all four limbs in a form of locomotion called 'knuckle-walking' but they can, and do, walk upright on occasions. They are shy, peaceful vegetarians who live in family groups consisting of a dominant adult male with several adult females and their children. Females are much less muscular.

The chimpanzees

The common chimpanzees more closely resemble humans than do the gorillas. Male chimpanzees are bigger and more muscular than the females. The common chimpanzee is also a knuckle walker, like gorillas. The natural habitat of chimpanzees includes both tropical forests and bordering savannas in west and central Africa.

Chimpanzees are intelligent animals with generally pleasant personalities. However, the males are less peaceful than the smaller females. This behaviour difference is typical of most primate species, including humans.

Bonobos are close relatives of common chimpanzees in the same genus, Pan. They are also called Pygmy chimpanzees, but, despite this name, they are only slightly smaller than the common chimpanzees. Bonobos usually have blacker hair with tufts at the side of their faces, longer arms and legs, as well as slimmer bodies. Within bonobo society copulation occurs frequently as a means of reducing tension in the community and has become recreational for them. In this and other traits, bonobos are much like humans.

The orangutans

Orangutans are the largest and the rarest of the Asian apes. When crossing from one tree to another both sexes usually cross direct by using branches; if there's a gap, they cross it by tree-swaying: that is, by grabbing a flexible stem, like a tall sapling, getting onto it, then making it sway back and forth, or round and round, with an ever-increasing distance until they can reach over to the next tree. They sometimes go down to the ground and walk, mostly quadrupedally i.e. on four limbs, but often bipedally.

Adult male and female orangutans are very different in appearance. Mature males have huge fleshy pads framing the upper part of their faces and females weigh only about half as much as the males.

Gorilla   *Chimpanzee*   *Ouragutan*   *Gibbon*

9

The Ape Species

The seven living species of Great ape are classified in four genera:

Subfamily Ponginae

Genus Pongo

Pongo pygmaeus with three subspecies:
North Western Bornean Orangutan, *Pongo pygmaeus pygmaeus*
Central Bornean Orangutan, *Pongo pygmaeus wurmbii*
North Eastern Bornean Orangutan, *Pongo pygmaeus morio*
Sumatran Orangutan, *Pongo abelii*

Subfamily Homininae

Genus Gorilla

Gorilla gorilla with two subspecies:
Western Lowland Gorilla, *Gorilla gorilla gorilla*
Cross River Gorilla, *Gorilla gorilla diehli*
Gorilla beringei with two subspecies:
Mountain Gorilla, *Gorilla beringei beringei*
Eastern Lowland Gorilla, *Gorilla beringei graueri*

Genus Pan

Pan troglodytes with five subspecies:
West African Chimpanzee, *Pan troglodytes verus*
Central Chimpanzee, or Tschego, *Pan troglodytes troglodytes*
Nigerian/Cameroon Chimpanzee, *Pan troglodytes elliotii*
Greater Eastern Chimpanzee, *Pan troglodytes schweinfurthii*
Lesser Eastern Chimpanzee, *Pan troglodytes marungensis*
Bonobo or Pygmy Chimpanzee, *Pan paniscus*. With no subspecies.

Genus Homo

Human, *Homo sapiens*. With no recognised subspecies.

The Lesser apes have 16 species in four genera

Subfamily Hylobatidae

Genus Hylobates

Lar gibbon, *Hylobates lar*
Kloss's gibbon, *Hylobates klossii*
Agile gibbon *Hylobates agilis*
Bornean White-bearded gibbon, *Hylobates albibarbis*
Pileated gibbon, *Hylobates pileatus*
Müller's gibbon, *Hylobates muelleri*
Silvery or Moloch gibbon, *Hylobates moloch*

Genus Hoolock

Hoolock gibbon, *Hoolock hoolock*
Eastern Hoolock gibbon, *Hoolock leuconedys*

Genus Nomascus

Yellow-cheeked gibbon, *Nomascus gabriellae*
Northern White-cheeked gibbon, *Nomascus leucogenys*
Southern White-cheeked gibbon, *Nomascus siki*.
Western Black Crested gibbon, *Nomascus concolor*
Cao-vit Crested gibbon, *Nomascus nasutus*
Hainan gibbon, *Nomascus hainanus*

Genus Symphalangus

Siamang, *Symphalangus syndactylus*

Orangutans are intelligent and generally peaceful animals. Most of the time, they live solitary lives browsing fruits and leaves. Some also create simple stick tools to get honey out of bee hives in tree crevices and they are known to use other tools.

The gibbons

The smallest and the most arboreal apes are the gibbons. Because of their small size, these members of the family Hylobatidae are also referred to as the "lesser apes". All gibbons are very slender, they have long bushy hair which makes them look bigger than they actually are. Unlike all the larger apes gibbon males and females are similar in size.

Hands and feet

All of the apes and most other primates have five fingers on each hand and five toes on each foot, they also have flat nails in place of rigid claws, making the manipulation of food and other objects much easier; but, probably the most important feature is the opposable thumb that is capable of being moved freely and independently and though present to some extent in all primates it is particularly highly developed in humans.

Humans, chimpanzees, orangutans and gorillas can also employ precision grips formed by pinching with the tips of their forefingers and thumb; this allows their hands to be used more effectively for manipulating even tiny objects. Gibbons use the thumb; to a lesser extent, but still use it to pick up food and for grooming.

Humans are, of course, the masters of manipulative dexterity, but chimpanzees are well known to use tools. Dr. Jane Goodall was

Hands and feet

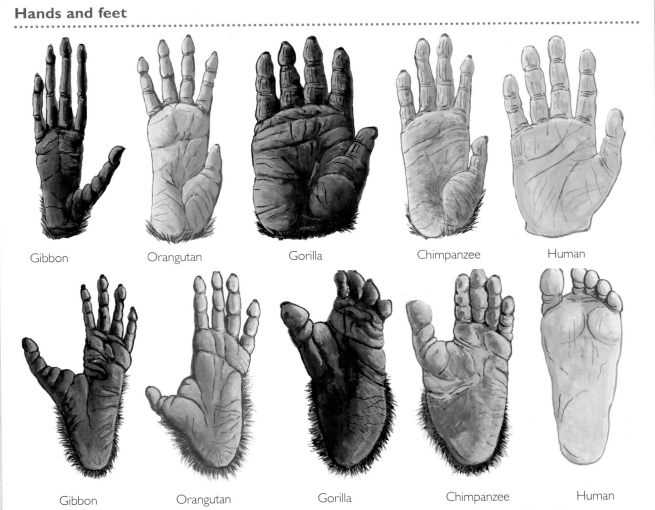

Gibbon   Orangutan   Gorilla   Chimpanzee   Human

Gibbon   Orangutan   Gorilla   Chimpanzee   Human

All primates, with the exception of humans, have prehensile feet in addition to hands, their toes are mobile and have very sensitive tactile pads at the tips, unlike most other mammals. The fifth digit, the 'thumb', is usually used for climbing but has been seen to be used to hold food when it is being torn apart, especially by chimpanzees.

the first to discover and report that chimpanzees make and use tools, an ability that was once only attributed to humans.

In her research in Gombe she noted that the chimpanzees used objects such as: stems, twigs, branches, leaves, and rocks in nine different ways to accomplish different tasks which assisted them in feeding, drinking, investigating out-of-reach objects, cleaning themselves and grooming others and as weapons.

Dr. Goodall also found that tool use is acquired through observational learning and is passed from one generation to the next. Orangutans are known to use tools, for example: Bornean orangutans have been observed using leaves as umbrellas to keep from getting wet and Sumatran orangutans have been observed making leaf gloves or cushions to protect themselves when consuming thorny foods. They both use leaves as sponges to help them drink water. They also use sticks to help knock fruit down from trees and as visual deterrents when threatened by shaking or throwing them. Gorillas and gibbons, having short thumbs and long fingers, are handicapped in relation to delicate manual dexterity but are adept in the coarser elements of hand use, particularly in relation to tree climbing and picking and handling food; gibbons are also known to use their thumbs as a probe. However, few have the high degree of thumb opposability and strength typical of humans.

Gorillas

Gorillas are the largest living primates and, together with the chimpanzee and orangutan, are the most closely related mammals to man. Proof of this, apart from appearance, has been provided by biochemical data and fossil comparison.

How many gorillas are there?

There are four kinds of gorilla distributed in two widely separated areas of west-central Africa. The Western Lowland gorilla inhabits the area around the Gulf of Guinea.

The Cross River gorilla inhabits the border between Nigeria and Camaroon. Eastern Lowland and Mountain Gorillas are found about a thousand miles to the east in eastern Congo (formerly Zaire), western Rwanda and western Uganda. In-between lies the Congo River and dense primary forest. No doubt, at one time, this distribution was continuous across central Africa but the primary forest does not have the ground vegetation necessary to support these largely terrestrial animals; added to this are the intrusions made by man which have caused the two species to be separated into their present localities.

The gentle giant

They have a generally formidable appearance and a past reputation for ferocity; but, thanks to the work of the American primatologists, George and Kay Schaller in 1959-1963, and of the late Dr Dian Fossey in the mid-sixties, the undeserved reputation of these gentle, intelligent creatures has largely been accepted as erroneous. Further proof of their gentleness can be learned from the 'Natural History of the Gorilla' by Dr Alan Dixson. Other valuable observations have been made by A. G. Goodall, Ian Redmond OBE and others. Lately, television programmes, showing them in close, friendly touch with human beings, especially with Sir David Attenborough, has added to the acceptance of their gentle nature.

What do they eat?

All the Gorillas are almost exclusively vegetarian. Their diet consists of the leaves, bark, stems, fruit and roots of over one hundred different types of herbs, vines and parts of trees, although the Western Lowland gorilla and the Cross River gorilla have been found to be more frugivorous than the other two subspecies.

Habitat

Groups number from between ten to over twenty-five. The males do not hold territorial boundaries and when neighbouring groups meet they usually mix in a friendly manner and then continue on their separate ways, another proof of their gentle nature.

Sleeping arrangements

Sleeping quarters, made from available herbage, are changed daily - adult males most often on the ground and females and juveniles in trees, but this varies regionally.

Mobility

Gorillas move by resting their weight on the middle joints of their fingers in a manner of locomotion known as 'knuckle–walking'. The skin of the knuckle joints, palms of the hands and the soles of the feet is very thick.

Communication

Studies have been made into gorilla communication which show that the males seem to be the most vociferous, using a series of grunts, hoots, screams and roars. The young whine and chuckle but do scream to a lesser degree when excited or frightened. It is thought also that 'chest thumping' is involved as a means of communication.

Sexual maturity

Generally, males reach sexual maturity between the ages of 7 and 11 years but the huge size and the silvering of the back doesn't come untill much later - perhaps 13+ years in Mountain gorillas, maybe even later, 17 years or so, in Western Lowland gorillas according to a recent paper by Thomas Breuer of the Max Planck Institute for Evolutionary Anthropology. Females mature between 6 and 9 years. There appears to be no marked season for breeding.

When in oestrus the female offers herself to several males but it is the dominant male who usually succeeds in the mating. The gestation period is between 237 and 296 days and births occur at intervals of about 3 to 4 years. At birth the infants weigh between 1.8 kg (4lbs) and 2.5 kg (5.5 lbs), staying with their mother for up to 3 years.

The females make dutiful mothers and suckle for 2 to 3 years. The infant tries solid food at about 4 months. Adult males are called 'silverbacks' because a saddle of gray or silver-coloured hair develops on their backs with age.

Gorilla and man skeleton comparison

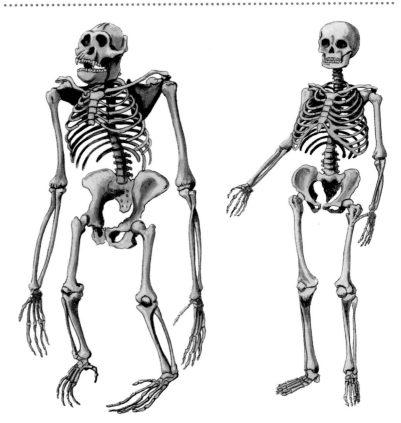

Comparison of the two skeletons shows the many similarities rather than the differences between *Gorilla* and *Homo sapiens*.

The Gorilla's head

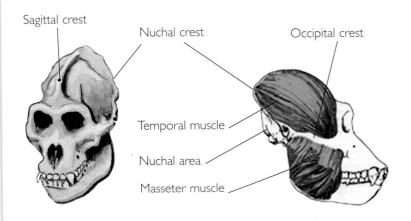

Sagittal crest

Nuchal crest

Occipital crest

Temporal muscle

Nuchal area

Masseter muscle

The huge size of the male gorilla necessitates proportionately larger teeth, especially molars, to sustain its intake of food which, in turn, means that the jaw muscles must also be proportionately larger. These muscles are called the Temporal muscles and they are attached to the tall bony crest called the Sagittal crest which is on the mid–line of the skull. Another muscle, the Masseter muscle, attaches to the Occipital crest and to the huge jawbone. The two crest bones give the adult male gorilla its distinctive high–domed appearance which is characteristic in all four gorillas. Female gorillas have smaller jaws than the males and therefore have a smaller Sagittal crest.
Illustrations taken from Dixson A.F. after Raven (1950) modified by Ray Hutchins.
Illustrations from Dixson A. F.

Comparisons of average body measurements of gorillas

Western Gorillas

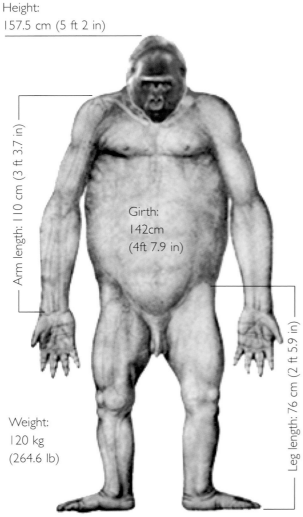

Height:
157.5 cm (5 ft 2 in)

Arm length: 110 cm (3 ft 3.7 in)

Girth:
142cm
(4ft 7.9 in)

Weight:
120 kg
(264.6 lb)

Leg length: 76 cm (2 ft 5.9 in)

Arm span: 231.5 cm (7 ft 7 in)

Cross River gorilla, *Gorilla gorilla diehli*

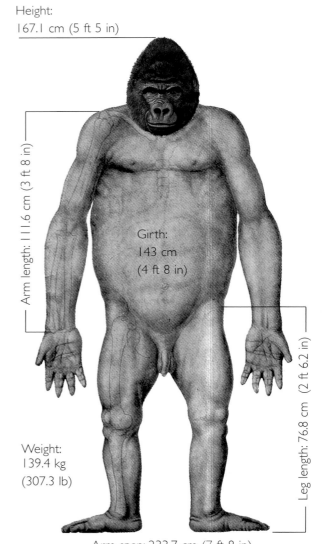

Height:
167.1 cm (5 ft 5 in)

Arm length: 111.6 cm (3 ft 8 in)

Girth:
143 cm
(4 ft 8 in)

Weight:
139.4 kg
(307.3 lb)

Leg length: 76.8 cm (2 ft 6.2 in)

Arm span: 233.7 cm (7 ft 8 in)

Western Lowland gorilla, *Gorilla gorilla gorilla*

Napier and Napier (1967), after Groves. Illustrations after Schultz, (1933) with additions by Ray Hutchins 2009. Dimensions from Dixson.

Eastern Gorillas

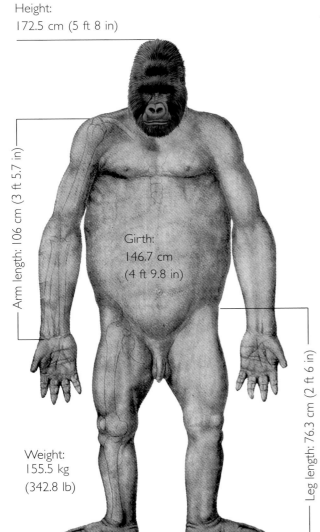

Height:
172.5 cm (5 ft 8 in)

Arm length: 106 cm (3 ft 5.7 in)

Girth:
146.7 cm
(4 ft 9.8 in)

Leg length: 76.3 cm (2 ft 6 in)

Weight:
155.5 kg
(342.8 lb)

Arm span: 227.5 cm (7 ft 5.6 in)

Mountain gorilla, *Gorilla beringei beringei*

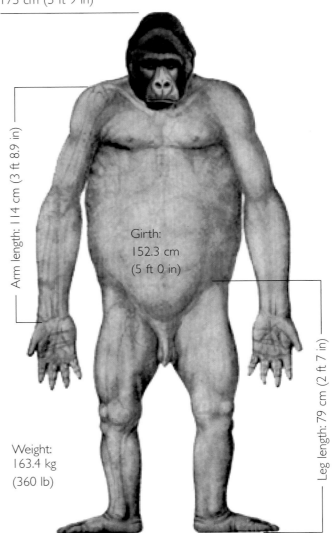

Height:
175 cm (5 ft 9 in)

Arm length: 114 cm (3 ft 8.9 in)

Girth:
152.3 cm
(5 ft 0 in)

Leg length: 79 cm (2 ft 7 in)

Weight:
163.4 kg
(360 lb)

Arm span: 259.5 cm (8 ft 6.2 in)

Eastern Lowland gorilla, *Gorilla beringei graueri*

The largest primate in the world

Napier and Napier (1967), after Groves. Illustrations after Schultz, (1933) with additions by Ray Hutchins 2009. Dimensions from Dixson.

The Western Lowland Gorilla
Gorilla gorilla gorilla

What's in a name

You will see that the Latin name for the Western Lowland gorilla has its generic name *Gorilla* (a noun) repeated for the specific name i.e. *Gorilla gorilla*. This is known as a *tautonym* and is derived from *tauton* (Gr) meaning 'the same', and, *onoma* (Gr) meaning 'a name'. Because the Western lowland gorilla is what scientists know as the nominate species – the one that was first described – it also carries the nominate subspecies name *of gorilla* – thus we have the full Scientific/Greek name of *Gorilla gorilla gorilla*.

Habitat

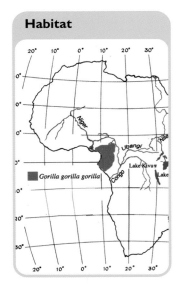

This is the gorilla that is most likely to be seen in zoos. It was the first to be known to science and was named as long ago as the fifth century BC in the writings of Hanno of Carthage, now modern Tunis. Hanno sailed the west coast of Africa and killed what he called 'gorillae' - 'hairy people' or 'wildman' - doubtless a native African name originally.

Where they live

Although having been known longer to science and in captivity lack of field-work has made it difficult to show its detailed distribution; however, they generally inhabit areas in Cameroon, Equatorial Guinea, Gabon, Central African Republic, Angola (Cabinda), and western Democratic Republic of Congo.

Since gorillas cannot swim, the River Congo (formerly the River Zaire), together with a thousand miles or more of primary forest, forms an effective eastern limit to their range.

How they differ

Although shorter in stature than the Mountain gorilla the arms and legs of the Western Lowland gorilla are a little longer; so, it has a slightly wider span than the Mountain gorilla, but not so wide as the Eastern Lowland gorilla.

The body, arms and legs are a uniform brownish-grey with a slight reddish tinge, especially on the head where, in some individuals, it becomes quite auburn. This compares to the much blacker colouring of the two eastern gorillas. The hair is much shorter than on the Mountain gorilla or the Eastern Lowland gorilla and the silvering on the backs of the adult male is more extensive, reaching from the shoulder blades to the rump and thighs.

The nasal septum (the projection around the nostrils) has irregularly bordered, flat, flared, swellings which reach the lips, giving it the notably different facial appearance to the other gorillas. The jaws and teeth are smaller in this gorilla as is the sagittal crest (q.v.); this could be because their diet is more frugivorous with up to 40% of their diet consisting of

Did you know? ...
The big toe of the Western Lowland gorilla is spread apart more than that of the Mountain gorilla. This is considered to be because the Mountain gorilla is slightly more terrestrial than the Western Lowland gorilla.

fruit; and, hence, the muscles do not have to contend with so much of the fibrous food taken by the eastern subspecies.

Social groups

The average size of the social groups is thought to be from six to eight but there is little observation, up until now, by field-workers and so the figures are estimated; although it is generally agreed that Western Lowland gorilla groups are smaller than either the Eastern Lowland gorilla or Mountain gorilla groups.

Chest beating

All subspecies of gorilla are well known for their curious chest-beating which is accompanied first of all by hooting and then by ritualistic feeding, standing vertically, pulling up vegetation and then by thumping the ground. This behaviour is carried out

Foot comparison between the Western Lowland Gorilla *(left) and the Mountain* Gorilla (right).

mostly by adult males but all sexes and ages are known to posture similarly.

Birth and infancy

Females give birth after a gestation period of up to 9 months. Breastfeeding lasts for about 2 to 3 years. The baby can crawl at around 9 weeks old and can walk at about 35 weeks old. The infant gorilla normally stays with its mother for 3 to 4 years and matures at around 11 to 12 years.

Conservation threats

There are two main causes for the decline in the Western Lowland gorilla, they are: commercial hunting and the Ebola virus. Since the early 1980s vast tracts of previously inaccessible forest have been penetrated by logging roads, which provide ready access to commercial hunters who provide bushmeat to the logging employees who actually eat more bushmeat than do local villagers. Since the early 1990s, Ebola has caused a massive number of gorilla and chimpanzee deaths in remote forest areas at the heart of their range.

Conservation efforts

Conservation areas exist in most gorilla ranges and several National Parks have been created recently, but extensive resources are required for a better understanding of the spread of the Ebola disease to allow development of a pro-active campaign to protect both gorilla and human populations through vaccination and/or the reinforcement of effective physical barriers.

Head of Mountain gorilla

Head of Western
Lowland gorilla

**The Western
Lowland Gorilla**
Gorilla gorilla gorilla

The Cross River Gorilla
Gorilla gorilla diehli

Status

The IUCN - The World Conservation Union classifies this gorilla as Critically Endangered (2008, CRA4cd), and is listed in CITES Appendix I since 1977

What's in a name

In 1904, Paul Matschie, a mammalian taxonomist working at the Humboldt University Zoological Museum named the subspecies *Gorilla g. diehli* in honour of Mr. Diehl, an employee of the German Northwestern Cameroon Company, who had collected the gorilla skulls on which Matschie based his new subspecies.

The Cross River Gorilla is a subspecies of the Western Lowland gorilla and they were identified as such in 1904 by Paul Matschie, a mammalian taxonomist working at the Humboldt University Zoological Museum in Berlin.

He described them as a new species of gorilla inhabiting the watershed of the Cross River in what was then German Cameroon. He noticed that this gorilla has a smaller skull than the Western Lowland gorilla *Gorilla g. gorilla* with a short row of molars, a different palate shape, skull base shape and smaller sagittal crest, these distinguished the Cross River gorilla *Gorilla g. diehli* as a subspecies.

Where they live

The most northern and western gorilla, Cross River gorillas are restricted to the border between Nigeria and Cameroon, in both tropical and subtropical moist broadleaf forests of the Obudu Plateau and other areas of Bamenda Highlands. Some of these areas are surrounded by sizeable human communities. Both of these areas once supported a montane forest ecosystem, since lost to grassland, and this could have been the reason that they evolved with the different physical attributes. Areas of habitation that they choose seem to be more to do with human pressure than types of habitat. They live in low-lying and submontane tropical and subtropical broadleaf forests, at between 200 to 2,000 metres altitude.

Areas of habitation in Nigeria are in the rugged, rocky, Afi and Mbe mountains and the higher reaches of the Asache and Mache rivers. In Cameroon they are found in the hilly Takamanda, Mone and Mbulu forests. These areas are over 200 km from the nearest Western lowland gorillas. However, they are rarely seen because they are very wary of local hunters.

How they differ

The unique features of the skull and dentition imply that these gorillas consume smaller food items that require less chewing but may be harder than those eaten by Western lowland gorillas and so need stronger masticatory forces. The incisors are used for biting rather than chewing.

These differences are as great between them and the Western Lowland gorillas than between the two types of eastern gorilla. Cross River gorillas have shorter hands and feet than other gorillas and the high opposability index are all suggestive of a more terrestrial life style.

These differences could be associated with lower fruit abundance or periods of fruit scarcity during prolonged dry seasons.

Did you know? ...

The Cross River gorilla is one of the 25 most endangered primates worldwide, according to the IUCN's Red List this gorilla is Critically Endangered. This is the highest ranking for species or subspecies that remain in the wild, and means that the population has decreased, or will decrease, by 80% within three generations. Fewer than 300 individuals are estimated to exist in the wild.

Population threats

Cross River gorilla populations are threatened by:

● habitat loss due to local illegal logging; expansion of agriculture;
● oil palm plantations; road networks;
● killing for the bushmeat trade;
● traditional medicine and trophies and
● they are also at risk due to the highly fragmented distribution of their very small numbers; if further encroachment into their habitat continues, inbreeding and loss of genetic variation will occur and will imperil their isolated groups.

This loss of habitat, the increased popularity of bushmeat and human diseases etc. have contributed heavily to the decline of this gorilla.

Conservation efforts

Conservation efforts and protection in Nigeria include the Cross River National Park, Okwangwo Division, the Mbe Mountains and the Afi Mountain Wildlife Sanctuaries. The conservation efforts in Cameroon include the Takamanda Forest Reserve and Mone River Forest Reserves. The Wildlife Conservation Society supports Cross River gorilla conservation and research programs i n both Cameroon and Nigeria.

Habitat

Gorilla gorilla diehli

The Cross River Gorilla
Gorilla gorilla diehli

The Mountain Gorilla
Gorilla beringei beringei

What's in a name

The Latin name for the Mountain gorilla has its generic name *Gorilla* (a noun). The specific name *beringei* is repeated for the subspecies name *beringei*. The species name is after Captain Robert von Beringe, an officer of the German Army, in what was then known as German East Africa, in 1902.

Habitat

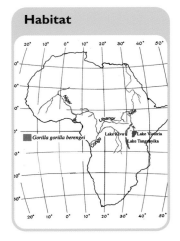

This is the gorilla made famous by the studies of Dr. Dian Fossey and in her book 'Gorillas in the Mist'.

Where they live

The range of the Mountain gorilla has been clearly defined. There are two populations. One is found in the Virunga volcanic mountains of Central Africa, within 3 national parks: Mgahinga Park, in south-west Uganda; Parc National des Volcans, in north-west Rwanda and Virunga National Park, in the eastern Democratic Republic of Congo (DRC). There are approximately 420 individuals found in the Virungas.

The other area of Mountain gorilla habitation is found in Uganda's Bwindi Impenetrable National Park where there are approximately 300 individuals.

Some consider the Bwindi population in Uganda is a separate subspecies, but at present this is still being debated.

These habitats occur in the Albertine Rift montane cloud forests of the Virunga Volcanoes, ranging in altitude from 2,225 to 4,267 m (7,300-14,000 ft). Most are found on the slopes of three of the dormant volcanoes: Karisimbi, Mikeno, and Visoke. The vegetation is very dense at the bottom of the mountains, becoming more sparse at higher elevations, and the forests where the Mountain Gorilla lives are often cloudy, misty and cold.

How they differ

The hair covering on the Mountain gorilla is thick and long, especially on the arms and legs. This is especially because of its mountain habitat with wet conditions and the cool temperatures at night. The coat has a distinct blue-black colouring. The 'silvering' on the backs of the adult males is more pronounced than on other gorillas because of the contrast of the body colour and is restricted to an area from the lower shoulder blades to the hips.

The face is shorter and broader than the lowland subspecies with the smaller nose having border swellings nearly semicircular and regular. The Bwindi population has less facial hair, especially on the eyebrows, and less pronounced nose swellings than the Virunga population.

The males of all Mountain gorillas have a large sagittal crest (q.v.).

The arms and legs are distinctly shorter than the lowland gorillas and the arrangement of the big toe differs in that it is more closely aligned with the other toes, more like the human configuration (see page 17).

The Mountain Gorilla is primarily terrestrial and quadrupedal. However, it will climb into fruiting trees if the branches can carry its weight, and it is capable of running bipedally up to 6 m (20 ft). Research carried out by Dr. Craig Stanford has found that the Bwindi gorillas, even silverbacks, are more likely to climb trees than those in the Virungas to feed on foliage, fruits, and epiphytes.

Did you know? ...

The Karisoke Research Center (sic), is situated between Mt. Karisimbi and Mt. Visoke in Rwanda's Virunga mountains. It was founded over 40 years ago by Dr. Dian Fossey and operated since her death by the Dian Fossey Gorilla Fund International. The Center is famed throughout the world as a focus for the study and protection of the critically endangered mountain gorillas. Karisoke's local guards diligently destroy and remove about 1,000 snares each year and help bring poachers to justice. The national park staff see to the veterinary needs and visitor control throughout the gorilla habitat and have involvement with the local people.

What do they eat?

Primarily herbivore, the majority of their diet is composed of the leaves, shoots and stems of 142 plant species. They also feed on bark, roots, flowers, and fruit, as well as small invertebrates. Adult males can eat up to 34 kg (76.5 lb) of vegetation a day, while a female can eat as much as 18 kg (40.5 lb). Similar to the other three races of gorilla they never stay long enough at one feeding place to strip it completely but crop the vegetation leaving enough to aid rapid regeneration.

Daily habits

The Mountain Gorilla is diurnal, most active between 6:00 a.m. and 6:00 p.m. Many of these hours are spent eating, as large quantities of food are needed to sustain its massive bulk. It forages in the early morning, rests during the late morning and around midday, and in the afternoon it forages again before resting at night.

They build 'nests', platforms of vegetation, to keep them off the cool and wet ground, with fresh 'nests' made each night. Only infants sleep in the same nest as their mothers. They leave their sleeping sites when the sun rises at around 6 am, except when it is cold and overcast; then they often stay longer in their nests.

Their gentle nature

Television programmes in the United Kingdom, with Sir David Attenborough, Dr. Charlotte Uhlenbroek, Ian Redmond OBE and others, have clearly shown the gentle nature of these wonderful animals.

Conservation

Considering that there are only about 720 Mountain gorillas left in the wild it is of paramount importance that conservation should be of top priority, otherwise we will lose these wonderful cousins of ours forever.

Rwandan Mountain gorilla male

Bwindi Mountain gorilla male

Rwanda Mountain gorilla female

Bwindi Mountain gorilla female

The Mountain Gorilla
Gorilla beringei beringei

Photographs by Ian Redmond

The Eastern Lowland Gorilla
Gorilla beringei graueri

What's in a name

The Scientific name for the Eastern lowland gorilla has its generic name *Gorilla* (a noun) The specific name has been changed from *gorilla* to *beringei*. The subspecies name *graueri* is after Robert Grauer who shot specimens in the mountains west of Lake Tanganyika early in the 20th century.
Dr. George Beals Schaller (born 1933) is a mammalogist, naturalist, conservationist and author, who first researched this gorilla.

This is the largest non-human primate in the world. Its name, Eastern Lowland gorilla, is something of a misnomer for although it lives mostly in lowland rain forested areas it is also found in mountainous areas like Tsiaberimu and the mountains Kahuzi and Biega. Other distribution lies west of Lake Kivu between the Lowa and Lugulu Rivers in the Utu region; in Mwega-Fizi region, south of Lake Kivu and northward in the Angumu region near the Maiko River, all in the Democratic Republic of Congo (formerly Zaire).

Massive size

The body is very much broader than both the Mountain and the Western Lowland gorilla and in all respects it is a much more massive animal. The colour is greyish-black with a slight brownish tinge with little or no hair on the chest, face, hands and feet. The 'silvering' on the male is confined to the back where the hair is shorter than on the arms and legs, but the hair, although long, is not as long as that of the Mountain gorilla.

Physical differences

The most obvious difference between this and the Western Lowland and Mountain gorilla is the extraordinary elongated face, slender nose, regularly bordered nasal swellings and longer jaw to accommodate the longer palate and canine teeth.

What they eat

These facial differences can be attributed to their diet which consists mostly of leaves, bark and stems of vines, herbs and parts of trees, necessitating the large teeth and powerful muscles attached to the sagittal and nuchal crests needed to

> **Did you know? ...**
> The Eastern Lowland gorilla is the largest of the four gorillas. The average height of an adult silverback male is approximately 175 cm (5 ft 9 in) to 183 cm (6ft 0 in) with an arm length of about 114 cm (3 ft 8.9 in), the arm span can reach to 259.9 cm (8 ft 6 in). Legs are 79 cm and the girth is 152.3 cm compared to the 146.7 cm of the Mountain gorilla, the 143 cm of the Western Lowland gorilla and the 142cm (4ft 7.9 in) of the Cross River gorilla. Their weight exceeds that of the other races being in the order of 163.4 kg (360.2 lb) in the average adult male, but can reach up to 225 kg (500 lb) with about half that for the female. From A. F. Dixson, The Natural History of the Gorilla

masticate the fibrous nature of their food.
They are known to eat only a few leaves from a single plant, allowing the plant to regrow. They will also eat fruit, seeds, bamboo shoots and insects.

Skull of male Eastern Lowland gorilla showing the large sagittal crest.

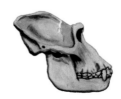
Skull of male Western Lowland gorilla with smaller sagittal crest.

Skull of female Eastern Lowland gorilla.

Skull of female Western Lowland gorilla.

Social groupings

The social groups are generally larger than in the other gorilla races with groups as large as 25 individuals having been seen, although the average is nearer 10 or 11. There is usually only one silverback in each group although this does vary where up to four silverbacks have been observed on rare occasions.

Birth and infancy

Females give birth to twins or a single infant after a gestation period of up to 9 months. Breastfeeding lasts for about 2 to 3 years. The baby can crawl at around 9 weeks old and can walk at about 35 weeks old. The infant gorilla normally stays with its mother for 3 to 4 years and they mature at around 11 to 12 years.

Conservation threats

As yet there has been no full survey of all populations of the Eastern Lowland gorilla so their numbers can only be approximate, and even though there are more Eastern Lowland gorillas than there are Mountain gorillas, the eastern race is unlikely to survive the encroachments of human impact unless reserves are created to protect these wonderful animals. Following a decade of civil war in the Democratic Republic of the Congo new estimates suggest that the number of Eastern Lowland gorillas may have plummeted by 70 percent. This conflict, illegal mining for a mineral used for electronic-device components and the growing bush-meat trade have all taken their toll according to conservation groups.

Habitat

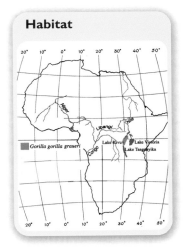

The Eastern Lowland Gorilla
Gorilla beringei graueri

Chimpanzees

Best known of all the primates, the chimpanzee is, apart from visual comparisons, by proof of biochemical data and fossil comparison, the most closely related mammal to humans. They are the most well known of all the primates because they are the species most commonly kept in zoos and exhibited on stage, screen and on television. Their similarities to man extend to tool-making, hunting and aggressive male behaviour - actions thought once to be uniquely human.

There are now four recognised subspecies of 'common' chimpanzee and a separate species, the Bonobo, or Pygmy chimpanzee, which, despite its name, does not differ markedly in length to 'common' chimpanzee; although it has a distinctly lighter build, weighing up to 35 kg less in males and 40 kg less in females than any of the mature common chimpanzee subspecies.

The 'common' chimpanzee has been known since the late 17th Century when as many as 14 species were recognised!

Distribution

They are distributed across west-central Africa ranging from Senegal eastwards to Uganda and Tanzania, north of the River Congo including Nigeria and Cameroon. They live not only in primary forest but also in areas of savanna woodland; here evergreen trees exist in clumps along protected gullies, a similar habitat to that thought to have been used by our ancestors. The bonobo inhabits an area confined to central Congo between the River Congo (formerly Zaire) and southward towards the River Kasai.

Brainpower and senses

Intelligence tests have shown how chimpanzee use their relatively large brains. They show that they have the ability to use words defined by hand signals similar to the sign languages used by deaf people; but, in the wild, they are also known to have methods of natural communication which are not too short of our own in complexity, and very superior to any

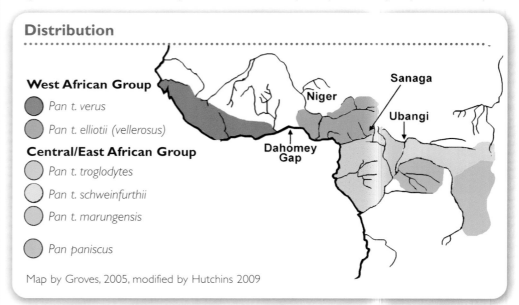

Distribution

West African Group
- Pan t. verus
- Pan t. elliotii (vellerosus)

Central/East African Group
- Pan t. troglodytes
- Pan t. schweinfurthii
- Pan t. marungensis
- Pan paniscus

Niger
Sanaga
Ubangi
Dahomey Gap

Map by Groves, 2005, modified by Hutchins 2009

Did you know? ...
Scientists have found that humans are 99% similar to the chimpanzee.

other mammal. They are able to solve complex problems and make and use tools for a variety of purposes. Indeed, so alike are they to us that up to 99% of their genetic material is said to be identical to that of *Homo sapiens*. Their sensory capabilities are similar to humans; their sense of touch may be slightly inferior but their sense of smell appears more acute.

Hunting and meat eating
Other than humans, chimpanzee are the only primate species to hunt other mammals in a deliberate and organised fashion. The hunt is carried out by the males only; it starts when the prey is sighted by an individual who will alert others to join him to chase the prey, others spread out to surround the prey whilst two or three wait in ambush. The chasers make a sudden dash towards the victim making them run into the arms of the waiting males in ambush.

The many facial expressions are similar to those of humans. Here is the fear defence look.

Their favourite prey appears to be the red colobus monkey but duiker, juvenile bushbuck and other small forest antelopes, are favoured alternatives.

Sleeping arrangements
Nests are made in trees at dusk with a fresh nest each night. A firm foundation is chosen and smaller branches are bent over and kept in place by the feet; finally small leafy twigs are tucked in around the rim of the nest; individuals have been observed picking handfuls of leafy twigs to place under their heads or other parts of the body. Chimpanzees never foul their sleeping quarters and are known to defecate and urinate over the edge of their nests, even in the middle of the night.

Social groupings
Chimpanzees live in communities of up to 120 members in areas between 10 to 50 sq km. The communities are broken up into sub-groups of from three to six in common chimpanzees and from 6 to 15 in bonobos. These never remain the same but fluctuate between all male, all female or all young groups and with different variations between ages and sexes; each animal having its own basic 'core' area where it rests and spends most of its time. None of these are true family groups. The damaging effects of inbreeding are avoided by the females leaving their community when they reach puberty and first oestrus; they then join a new community close by, taking their young with them; they are then protected by their new male consorts.

Communication
Because chimpanzees live in these complex family groups, they use a wide range of auditory, visual, and tactile signals adapted both for distant and close communication. Chimpanzees are claimed to be the noisiest of all African animals! These loud calls enable them to wander

This is the thinking, querying, look.

Here is 'thoughtful' look.

Did you know? ...
Chimpanzees can reach 50 years of age in captivity

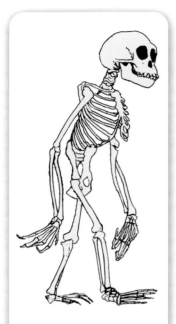

Chimpanzee skeleton showing the similarities with humans in general make-up; but, note the very much longer arms and shorter legs.

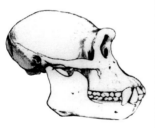

Chimpanzee skull shows similarities to early anthropoids. Note the lack of the sagittal crest

far within their territory and still stay in contact with community members.

Studies have shown that chimpanzees have 32 different calls that are versions of 4 call types: grunts, barks, screams, and hoots. The famous "pant-hoot" is a call that chimpanzees use to signal their sex and individual identity. This call begins with breathy, low-pitched hoots that then goes into a series of quicker, higher-pitched in-and-out pants. Finally the pant-hoot builds to a loud climax. Both male and female chimpanzees make the pant-hoot call with high-ranking adult males pant-hooting most frequently.

Chimpanzees also cry, whimper, lip smack and tooth clack to express their emotions or feelings.

Dr. Jane Goodall, in her study of the subspecies *P.t. marunguensis*, in the Gombe Stream Chimpanzee Reserve, (now a National Park) which is on the eastern shore of Lake Tanganyika north of Kigoma in Tanzania, reported a wide range of calls that were certainly communicative but, as she points out in her remarkable book on the chimpanzee, '*In the Shadow of Man*', they have not learned that great advance in the evolution of man - the power of speech.

Facial expressions

Chimpanzees are very sensitive to facial expressions, including eye movements, which are very much like human expressions. They constantly look for different facial expressions from other members of the group to discover their moods and intentions.

Sexual maturity

Male chimpanzees reach sexual maturity between 8 and 10 years and become fully adult between 11 and 13 years, with females becoming mature between 11 and 13 years giving birth for the first time at around 13 to 15 years. There appears to be no breeding season. Females mate only when in

This sad chimpanzee was saved by The Limbe Wildlife Centre which is situated in the small fishing town of Limbe at the foot of Mount Cameroon. This organisation saves many species from Cameroon that include the diehli gorilla and many other primates. In providing sanctuary to confiscated wild animals, the LWC also carries out conservation education programmes for local communities. Cameroon, where LWC does its work, boasts the second highest levels of Primate biodiversity in Africa and is home to many locally endemic and critically endangered primates such as the elliotti chimpanzee, and the diehli gorilla.

heat (oestrus) when their sexual skin becomes swollen and brightly coloured. At that time they will mate with several males as many as six times a day. Towards the end of the oestrus period, at the time of ovulation, mature males will compete until one is chosen as a 'consort'. The male and female then leave the group. Most pregnancies result from this 'honeymoon'.

Birth and infancy

The gestation period is between 230 and 240 days and the young are born weak and helpless. For the first few days the baby is supported by its mother's hand but soon begins to cling to its mother's underside unassisted. At 5-7 months it begins to ride on her back and at 4 years the infant follows its mother on foot staying with her for up to 7 years.

Weaning is started in the third year. The females remain unreceptive for 3-4 years after giving birth.

Likeness to man

The genus Pan is now considered to be part of the subfamily to which humans also belong. This species is the closest living evolutionary relative to humans They share a common ancestor with humans from six million years ago. Research has found, through DNA tests, that there is up to 99% DNA which is identical between human beings and chimpanzees, It has even been suggested that the 'common' chimpanzees *troglodytes* and the bonobo *paniscus* belong with humans *sapiens* in the genus *Homo*, rather than in *Pan*! One argument for this is that other species have been reclassified to belong to the same genus on the basis of even less genetic similarity than that between humans and chimpanzees.

Fossil records

Many human fossils have been found in East Africa, but chimpanzee fossils were only found in West and Central Africa. These were not described until 2005. so they did not appear to overlap with the major human fossil sites. However, some chimpanzee fossils have now been found from Kenya, dating from the Middle Pleistocene period, so it could be that both were present in the East African Rift Valley during this time and would indicate that both humans and members of the early chimpanzees were present together.

Field studies

In the 1960s three field studies were made of the common chimpanzee by Dr Adriaan Kortlandt in 1960, Dr. Jane Goodall from 1961-1963 and by Vernon and Frances Reynolds in 1962; until then very little was known about their way of life in their natural environment.

Dr. Jane Goodall began studying the Kasakela chimpanzee community in Gombe Stream National Park, Tanzania in 1960 and with her patience and optimism she discovered much of the nature of chimpanzees that was previously unknown. In 1977, she established the Jane Goodall Institute (JGI), which supports the Gombe research, and she is a global leader in the effort to protect chimpanzees and their habitats.

A population of wild chimpanzees in the Budongo Forest, Uganda, was studied between September, 1966, and March, 1967.

The bonobo has been studied by the American Dr. Jo Thompson since 1992. Although little is known of bonobos in detail in the wild, they were first described as a separate species in 1929 by studies from museum specimens. Dr. Jo Thompson established the Lukuru Wildlife Research Foundation (LWRP) in 1992 in the Democratic Republic of Congo (then called Zaire) a territory of almost 24,000 square kilometres in the middle of this vast country. Then, in 1998, she bought 34 square kilometres of virgin terrain in the southern half of the LWRP and created the Bososandja Faunal Reserve.

There have been other studies of the bonobo, amongst them being that carried out by Frans B. M. de Waal who is a research professor at the Yerkes Regional Primate Research Center in Atlanta and professor of psychology at Emory University.

Map showing study areas

The Western Chimpanzee
Pan troglodytes verus

This Chimpanzee, *Pan troglodytes verus*, has a high and narrow head with the muzzle projecting strongly with large prominent ears. The flesh-coloured palms and soles have some dark spots. The face of older animals is dark, spotted, becoming black, but with the spots still distinguishable. The ears become a bronze colour with age. Old males develop a whitish beard.

What's in a name

The Latin name: *Pan* (formerly *Anthropopithecus*) is an Ancient Greek word from mythology, where Pan was the god of pastures and woods in Arcadia; it means 'all, the whole'. Two Ancient Greek words make up the name troglodytes: *trogle* means a hole and *dutes* means a burrower, a diver; which, together means *troglodyte*, a cave-dweller. This is rather a misnomer because chimpanzees do not live in caves.

The Latin *verus* means: true, real, genuine. This subspecies is also known as the True Chimpanzee; the reason for this is unknown.

The face of the young is flesh-coloured with some dark spots and a dark, bluish, mask around the eyes and above the nose. The hair of the head has a central parting. Up to 3 years old they have white hair tufts above their buttocks.

Distribution
Their distribution stretches across Burkina Faso; Côte d'Ivoire; Ghana; Guinea; Guinea-Bissau; Liberia; Mali; Senegal; Sierra Leone.

Social groups
The size of the social groups is up to 60 and sometimes even up to 80 animals. During the day they split up into small groups, so that the whole tribe is seldom seen together. Some males are solitary.

Sexual maturity
In males begins between 8 and 10 years with full adulthood between 11 and 13 years. Females become sexually mature between 8 and 9 years. There is no marked breeding season but most births occur from August to November. Like the other common chimpanzee females, the vulva is placed in a posterior position, which becomes brightly coloured and swollen during oestrus. The oestrous cycle lasts between 35 to 41 days and, when on heat, the females may be mated by all of the sexually mature males of the group in succession. The mating lasts only a few seconds. The gestation period lasts on average from 227 to 232 days with usually a single birth, twins are not rare; but both seldom survive.

What they eat
The main food of all chimpanzees is made up mainly of all the products of plants, especially the fruits. This diet is supplemented by at least 5% of animal prey, especially of social insects, termites and ants, and caterpillars, which they collect directly by hand or with specially prepared tools.

Tool use
These chimpanzees are remarkably dextrous; they have been seen to strip twigs to enable them to 'fish' for termites, and, to insert the stick into Driver Ants nests and wait for the ants to cling to the stick in attack, they then lick them off the stick like a lollipop!

Another tool use is to break open hard shells with heavy sticks or rocks against a chosen 'anvil'. They also make sponges of screwed-up, chewed, leaves or bark, to get water from tree boles; and, have been known to manufacture fly-whisks. They also hunt the young of

> **Did you know? ...**
> The Western chimpanzee, Pan t. verus, stands a little over 120 cm (3 ft 9in) in height, with the males having an arm span of nearly 180 cm (5 ft 11in). Weight in the wild is 48.9 kg (108 lb) for males and 40.6 kg (89.5 lb) for females, making it a heavier and larger animal than the eastern chimpanzees.

pigs, antelopes, monkeys and baboons; and, will use a stick to spear bushbabies. On very rare occasions they eat their own young,

Conservation threats

Habitat loss, from mining, forestry and agriculture, is one of the major threats to *Pan troglodytes verus*. Deforestation in west Africa is most severe and remaining pockets of undisturbed forest are home to highly fragmented populations of this chimpanzee. The demand for bushmeat is increasing, due in part to the growing human population, more accessible forests and the increased availability of firearms; some conservationists believe this trade is currently the biggest threat to species' survival in the area. Exposure to human diseases presents a further threat to this chimpanzee.

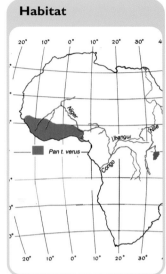

Habitat

Pan t. verus

The Western Chimpanzee
Pan troglodytes verus

The Central Chimpanzee or Tschego
Pan troglodytes troglodytes

Status

The IUCN - The World Conservation Union classifies this chimpanzee as Endangered (2008).

What's in a name

The species and subspecies Latin name, *troglodytes*, is here repeated because the Linnaean specific name later became the subspecies name, i.e., the species name became the name for the subspecies.

This chimpanzee differs from the other three subspecies by its very broad head and thickened brow ridges, which stretch right across the face. The profile is very concave. The muzzle is less broad than *P.t. verus* but broader than *P.t. schweinfurthii*. They are very similar to the other recognised subspecies in their habits.

Distribution

Their distribution stretches from the Sanaga River southwards through Cameroon, Gabon, Equatorial Guinea, Anglola (Cabinda) and the Republic of the Congo, to the Ubangui and lower Congo Rivers. These rivers form the boundaries of the three common chimpanzee territories with *Pan verus* to the west, and *schweinfurthii* many miles to the east. The divisions being made because chimpanzees do not usually swim but they are known to wade through rivers and swamps.

Adult balding

The skin colour of the face in the young is pink developing tan spots, which turns deep black in adults. The fur and skin is all deep black in maturity. The hair on the heads of the males thins out at a very early age, as does that on the females, who go totally bald right down to the temples.

Both sexes have a beard on the chin which is long but very sparse and white in colour. The sideburns are very long and hang down from the sides of the face. Juveniles have a white anal tuft.

Social grouping

The average size of the social groups is up to 60 and sometimes even up to 80 animals. During the day they split into small groups, so that the whole tribe is seldom seen together. These social groups differ in composition from rainforest dwelling animals in their 'core' areas, with all male or all female, or all female with young, groupings. Some males are solitary.

Sexual maturity and breeding

Sexual maturity, giving birth, weaning and infancy are all similar to the other 'common' chimpanzees and, as with

*Two tschegos enjoy freedom in a typical rainforest habitat.
Photo: Cyril Ruoso*

these, the females have the vulva placed in a posterior position, which becomes brightly coloured and swollen during oestrus.

What do they eat?

This chimpanzee is omnivorous but its diet is primarily vegetarian. The diet consists of fruits, leaves, nuts, seeds, tubers, and other vegetation. Termites are also eaten regularly in some populations. They also eat a variety of insects and hunt and kill smaller mammals for meat.

Carnivorous traits

They also hunt the young of pigs, antelopes, monkeys and baboons.

Tool use

These chimpanzees have been seen to take the bark from twigs and to insert the stick into driver ants and termite nests and wait for the insects to cling to the stick before licking them off.

Did you know? ...

When standing erect this chimpanzee stands between 100 cm to 170 cm (3 ft 3.4 in to 5 ft 7 in) in height, with the males having an arm span of nearly 180 cm (5 ft 11 in). Weight, in the wild, is between 34 kg to 50 kg. (75 to 110.2 lb) for males and 40.6 kg. (89.5 lb) for females, making it a heavier and larger animal than the Western chimpanzee P. t. verus.

They also break open hard shells with heavy sticks or rocks against a chosen 'anvil' and make sponges of screwed-up, chewed, leaves or bark, to collect water.

Habitat

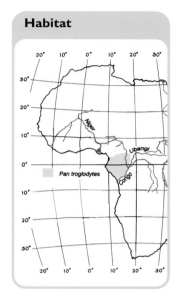

Pan troglodytes

The Tschego or Bald Chimpanzee
Pan troglodytes troglodytes

The Nigerian/Cameroon Chimpanzee
Pan troglodytes elliotii (formerly P. t. vellerosus)

What's in a name

The former name *vellerosus* means 'hairy' but John F Oates, Professor, Department of Anthropology, Hunter College and the Graduate School of the City University of New York, discovered that the type specimen was not from Nigeria or Cameroon but from Gabon, so he and Professor Colin Groves, School of Archaeology & Anthropology, Australian National University, Canberra, Australia, used the next available scientific name of *elliotti*.

The name *elliotti* derives from Daniel Giraud Elliot (1835-1915) who was one of the founders of the American Museum of Natural History in New York and the American Ornithologists' Union. He was also curator of zoology at the Field Museum in Chicago.

(Information: Professor Colin Groves)

The Nigeria/Cameroon chimpanzee is the most endangered of the currently recognised subspecies of chimpanzee in Africa.

Distribution

They inhabit the area between the Niger and Sanaga rivers across the boundaries of Nigeria and Cameroon.

Few studies

Relatively little is known of their ecology, behaviour, culture and conservation status - certainly compared to the other chimpanzee subspecies in Africa.

Discovery

They have been known to science since the 19th century. The earliest description comes from specimens collected by the German officer Lt. Jasper von Oerttzen.

Physical differences

Paul Matschie (1861-1926) was a German zoologist who worked at the Humboldt University Zoological Museum in Berlin. He provided further differences by details of 'the size of the ears, orientation of cheek whiskers, prominence of brow ridges, size of upper lip and patterns of baldness on the forehead'. However, these descriptions are based on a few skulls and the dried skins of one or two museum specimens, so they are not very helpful in understanding the physical differences between these and other chimpanzees. But some common characteristics are recognised and these include: small ears and much more abundant and softer fur, with the fur of the back being of a brown colour, and analyses of teeth and skulls reveal that the Nigerian/Cameroon chimpanzees have smaller teeth and skulls than surrounding chimpanzee populations, but whether these and other features can be used to differentiate this little-studied chimpanzee from others in Africa remains to be verified.

Boundary divisions

Population genetic analyses from samples collected throughout Nigeria and Cameroon indicate that the Sanaga River in central Cameroon separates the Nigerian-Cameroon chimpanzee *P. t. elliotii* from the Tschego, or Central chimpanzee *P. t. troglodytes* in southern Cameroon. This division at the Sanaga River appears to be quite ancient and the lineages of chimpanzees restricted to either side of the Sanaga shared a last common ancestor approximately 600,000 years ago.

There is additional evidence for population subdivisions of chimpanzees in western Africa: Chimpanzees from Upper Guinea, the Western chimpanzee, *P. t. verus*, and those from the Gulf of Guinea region, the Nigerian-Cameroon chimpanzee, *P. t. elliotii*, may be separated by either the Niger River or the Dahomey Gap.

Habitat

The Nigerian-Cameroon chimpanzees are found predominantly in moist forest, dry forests and forest galleries that extend into savannah woodlands

Tool use

Recent research work in the Ebo Forest in Cameroon has shown that these chimpanzees use stone tools to access nuts from Coula trees and also use sticks to hunt for insects, previously,

Did you know? ...

This chimpanzee stands a little over 120 cm (3 ft 11 in) in height. Weight, in the wild, is 48.9 kg (107.8 lb) for males and 40.6 kg (89.5 lb) for females.

this nut cracking behaviour had only been observed in the Western chimpanzee *P. t. verus* populations.

Conservation threats

Habitat loss, caused by Slash and burn agriculture, has led to deforestation across West and Central Africa. Logging and oil and gas mining have increased giving human accessibility to remote areas. Poaching and hunting for meat, the pet trade and for medicinal purposes add to the problem. The death of the mother is usual with the capture of infant chimpanzees for the pet trade or for medicinal purposes and the similarity of these chimpanzees to humans means that they are exposed to the many diseases that affect us.

Decline in numbers

It is currently estimated that the total population now is less than 6,500 individuals remaining (B. Morgan and J. Oates pers. comm. 2006) and they are separated into increasingly fragmented sub-populations throughout much of their former range. This high rate of decline will continue for the foreseeable future. Habitat fragmentation and the commercial bushmeat trade combine to make P. t. ellioti the most threatened chimpanzee subspecies, with the both the lowest population size and smallest distribution. Unless efforts are galvanised for the longer-term, the conservation outlook for this important animal is bleak.

Habitat

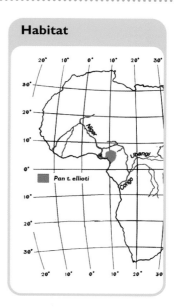

The Nigerian/Cameroon (Cross River) Chimpanzee
Pan troglodytes elliotii

The Eastern Chimpanzee
Pan troglodytes schweinfurthii and Pan t. marunguensis

What's in a name

The Latin: *Pan* (formerly *Anthropopithecus*) is an Ancient Greek word from mythology, where Pan was the god of pastures and woods in Arcadia; it means 'all, the whole'.

Jane Goodall would prefer *satyrus* which is the name for a woodland being 'half-human and half-bestial, attached to the train of Bacchus'. This name suits more the nature of the mischievous chimpanzee. This name was used for the chimpanzee in the early 20th century before it was found that *troglodytes* was an earlier name. The earliest name is always the one that should be used in scientific names.

Georg August Schweinfurth (1836-1925) was a German botanist who travelled in the interior of East Africa (from 1868) and studied the inhabitants together with the flora and fauna of the region

Schweinfurth was the 'discoverer' of this subspecies and it is referred to as 'Schweinfurth's chimpanzee' by some.

The derivation of the name *marunguensis* is from the Marungu district of southeastern DRC on the west side of Lake Tanganyika whence it was first described in the late 1800s.

This species is now divided into a north-western group - the "real" or Greater Eastern Chimpanzee P. t. schweinfurthii - and a south-eastern group, the Lesser Eastern chimpanzee, *P. t. marunguensis*. This sixth subspecies of common chimpanzee has been identified in a new study of chimpanzee skulls by Professor Colin Groves of the Australian National University in Canberra. He believes that *Pan troglodytes marunguensis* should join the five already recognised subspecies.

Comparisons between subspecies

The differences between the "real" Eastern chimpanzee, *P. t. schweinfurthii* and *P. t. marunguensis* are that the former have large skulls and broad braincases. *P. t. marunguensis* is relatively broader between the eyes, and with a relatively longer palate.

P. t. marungensis is also smaller, weighing 30 to 35 kg on average, compared with 50 to 60 kg for *P. t. schweinfurthii*.

In both subspecies skin colour in the young is pink, becoming black with maturity. The fur is predominantly black, long and sparse, but with adults having a mixture of blackish grey on the hips, thighs and chin, sometimes with a white beard.

Physical differences

The differences between these subspecies and *Pan t. verus*, *Pan t. troglodytes* and *Pan t. elliotii* are very noticeable. These Eastern chimpanzees have, in both the juvenile and the adult, a pink face with no speckling and with little contrast between the adults and young. Balding occurs on the male with a gradual thinning over a wide area, but, on the female, it never spreads to the temples or is ever widespread. There is hardly any parting and the sideburns are full and backswept. Males have a straggly, full, white beard.

The facial profile is less concave than in the other chimpanzees and the brow ridges tend to be thinner, straight

> **Did you know? ...**
> P. t. schweinfurthii *is similar in size to the other two 'common' chimpanzees, standing from 160 centimetres (5 ft 3 in) and females up to 130 cm (4 ft 3 in) in height. Weight between 40 and 65 kg (88 and 143 pounds)* P. t. marunguensis *is smaller than* P. t. schweinfurthii *and weighs between 30 to 35 kg (66-77 pounds).*

across, but not marked lateral to the eyes; the glabella, the portion immediately above the nose, is continuous with the brow ridges. The whole head form is more rounded than with the other subspecies and with a narrower muzzle. Only juveniles have the white tail tuft.

Common chimpanzee females have the vulva placed in a posterior position which becomes swollen, cyclically, during oestrus.

The males are strongly dominant and, in most cases, initiate copulation. There appears to be no homosexuality in either sex.

Social groups

The average size of the social groups is thought to be six, or less, and the sex ratio of the core group is thought to be two females to each male.

Distribution and habitat

The distribution of *P. t. schweinfurthii* stretches from the northern Republic

A juvenile chimpanzee, rescued by The Tusk Trust Chimfunshi Wildlife Orphanage in central Zambia, shows happiness in being well cared for. This organisation has saved many chimpanzees over the years.

of Congo, between the Ubangui and Congo rivers eastwards and southwards across a line roughly on the Equator. The distribution of *P. t. marunguensis* is in Uganda, Tanzania and southeast DRC, it stretches to the Budongo Forest, and southward between the Lualaba River and the east side of Lake Tanganyika, where the Gombe Stream Chimpanzee Reserve is situated. Their habitat is the rainforests, and other types of forest to over 3,000 ft. in the mountains, just below where the Mountain gorillas live.

Field studies

This chimpanzee (*marunguensis*) is famous for being the subject species in the field studies undertaken by Dr. Jane Goodall in the Gombe Stream Chimpanzee Reserve, in what is now Tanzania, in the early sixties. This subspecies can now be seen in many zoos.

Habitat

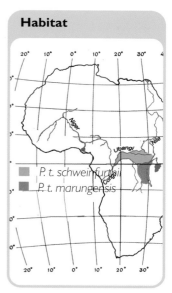

Pan t. schweinfurthii and P. t. marunguensis. Distribution map of the Eastern Long-haired chimpanzees

The Eastern or Long-haired Chimpanzee
Pan troglodytes schweinfurthii

The Bonobo or Pygmy Chimpanzee
Pan paniscus

What's in a name

The Latin name, for this species is *Pan* which is old Greek for 'all', 'the whole'. Pan was the rural god of pastures and woods in Arcadia in Greek mythology. The Latin species name *paniscus* means 'a small pan' where the suffix *-iscus* (L) means 'dim' or 'less'; this chimpanzee is also known as the Dwarf Chimpanzee.

A captive Bonobo using a tool to pick up food.
Copyright: Sheppard Software

Though they are genetically no more closely related to humans than the common chimpanzee (initial genetic studies have characterised their DNA as up to 99% identical to that of Homo sapiens), the Bonobo is considered to be the one whose behaviour most closely resembles that of humans, in fact more recent studies have shown that chimpanzees, in general, are more closely related to humans than to gorillas.

The name Bonobo first appeared in 1954, when Edward Tratz and Heinz Heck proposed it as a new and separate generic term for pygmy chimpanzees.

Where they live

They live in primary and secondary swampy forest areas from the southern part of the great Congo basin in the Democratic Republic of Congo, between the middle and upper Congo river to the Lualaba river in the east and south to the Lukenie river and a southern limit near to the Kasai river.

Human-like traits

Their predisposition for walking upright, their means of communication and their facial expressions make them, from an evolutionary and psychological perspective, the most important species in terms of what they reveal about human nature.

Physical differences

The Bonobo is considered to be a separate species to the common chimpanzee although the form and structure are closely similar.

The main differences are the black skin, red lips and mid-line hair parting, weaker eyebrow swellings and a slightly arched forehead. There is no sagittal crest. The nostrils are swollen and the ears are smaller than those of the other chimpanzees. They have a more elegant body with a narrower and more slender trunk with a proportionately longer arms and legs.

The legs are more slender and the feet are slimmer. They have a larger big

> ### Did you know? ...
> *The height of an adult male is between 90 to 100 cm (3 to 3.3 ft) and they weigh between 25 to 45 kg (55 to 99 lb). The males are a little larger and heavier than the females.*

toe and the second and third toes join at the base. They have little hair on the breast, inside arms and legs, otherwise the hair on the body is close-lying. They do not go bald as early in life as other chimpanzees. Perhaps the most important difference in the females is that the vulva is directed more forward than the females of the common chimpanzee.

Mating and birth

Sexual maturity is similar to the other chimpanzees with males becoming mature at between 8 to 10 years and fully adult between 11 and 13 years. Females become mature between 8 and 9 years.

Frontal mating is usual with the Bonobo and it is the females who encourage the males to mate. They will continue sexual activity during both pregnancy and lactation. The gestation period is between 8-8½ months and usually a single infant is born; twins are very rare.

The young are black at birth except that the flesh around the face, ears, palms and soles of feet are pink, becoming black with maturity. They sometimes have white anal tufts on their bottoms.

Sexual social bonds

Bonobos appear to be obsessed with sex. They use it as a casual greeting or to cement friendships. Males will mate with males, females with females and both even have genital contact with juveniles and even infants. Mating is usually face-to-face. As in humans, the importance of mating is beyond reproductive needs, it is used to form and strengthen social bonds between individuals.

A silent species

Unlike the common chimpanzee, the Bonobo, in the wild, is a quiet animal with no noisy behaviour and no noise when families meet. Sometimes they may make a high pitched alarm call. However, in captivity they use a wide range of, mostly high-pitched, sounds and can be quite noisy.

Family groups

They often gather in large family groups and will join, amicably, with other family groups.

Predators

The leopard could be a predator and monkey-eating eagles may be a danger to young Bonobos; but, at the sight of men and dogs they give a high-pitched warning call which then sends them scurrying, silently, through the forest canopy for some distance and then down to the forest floor to increase the distance between them and their only true enemy.

Conservation

Dr. Jo Thompson, the Director of the Lukuru Wildlife Research Project in the Democratic Republic of Congo, initiated, and has maintained, fieldwork studying the bonobos of this site for more than 16 years, focusing on ecology and conservation in alliance with the local people.

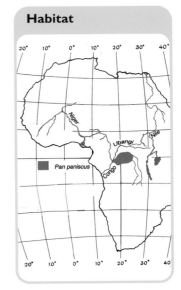

Habitat

Pan paniscus

The Bonobo or Pygmy Chimpanzee
Pan paniscus

Sleeping nests are similar to other chimpanzees but are made higher in the canopy up to 27 m (89 ft).

They move quickly, and with great agility, high in the forest canopy between 30 to 50 m (98 to 164 ft) high, where they collect and eat fruit in the early mornings and late afternoons. In between these times they descend to the ground to eat fallen fruit.

Orangutans

Orangutans are known for their intelligence, long arms and reddish-brown hair. According to research orangutans are one of the world's most intelligent animals other than humans, with the ability to solve problems and have an even higher learning capacity than chimpanzees.

They are currently found only in rainforests on the islands of Borneo and Sumatra, though fossils have been found in Java, Vietnam and China. Their name orangutan (also written orang-utan, orang utan) derives from the Malay and Indonesian phrase orangutan meaning "person" and hutan, meaning "forest" thus "person of the forest".

Physical size

The arms of an orangutan are twice as long as their legs and their length has to do with the longer radius and ulna rather than the relatively shorter humerus; they span over 2 m (6 ft 6 ins) from fingertip to fingertip. They have flexible hip joints and their hand-like feet make them appear to have four arms. The fingers and toes are curved, allowing better grip when they move through the trees, swinging from one branch to another, in a movement that is called brachiating.

How they walk

Orangutans walk on the ground by shuffling on their palms with their fingers curved inward; unlike gorillas and chimpanzees they are not knuckle-walkers.

Solitary lifestyle

They are more solitary than the other apes, with males and females generally coming together only to mate.

Male maturity

Adult male orangutans show two stages of physical development, namely flanged and unflanged. Flanged adult males have cheek pads, "flanges", and a throat pouch, these are absent from both adult females and from unflanged males.

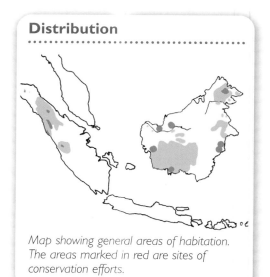

Distribution

Map showing general areas of habitation. The areas marked in red are sites of conservation efforts.

A flanged male establishes and protects a home range that does not overlap with other flanged males' home ranges; here he advertises his presence, with loud calls, and waits for receptive females to find him.

Male calls

Mature males have a large throat pouch that enables them to produce very loud, long calls that can carry through forests for up to 1 km (0.6 m). It is made up of a series of loud sounds followed by a bellow. These calls are also made to claim home range and keep out intruding males.

Unflanged males do not establish territories though they are able to reproduce; but, they seek out females in oestrus and force copulation. However, mature females will fend off these immature suitors, preferring to mate with a mature male.

Sometimes these immature appealing males make the transition from unflanged to flanged within a few months; they then are able to establish and defend a home range of their own.

Female maturity and reproduction

Females are mature and capable of continual reproducing, in the wild when they are between 12 to 14 years old. Their pregnancy lasts for up to 8½ months and they give birth to a single baby. These are weaned from their mothers after six or seven years.

Sleeping arrangements

The most arboreal of the great apes, orangutans spend nearly all of their time in the trees. At night they construct sleeping nests from branches and foliage. These nests are shared by a mother and her nursing offspring. They often use a leaf as a "roof" to protect themselves against rain. Sometimes they rest in these nests in the afternoon after a morning spent collecting food.

They sometimes have ischial callosities, fleshy, nerveless pads, attached to the hip bones which they sit on when they rest with their heads tucked under their arms on their chests

What do they eat?

Fruit makes up a large percentage of the orangutan diet, especially those with sugary or fatty pulp, like figs, but they also eat young leaves, shoots, flowers, seeds bark, insects and bird eggs.

Conservation threats

Habitat destruction is due to human activities. Serious concern is caused by the conversion of vast areas of tropical rainforest to the international demand for palm oil. This oil is used for cooking, cosmetics, mechanics, and more recently as source of biodiesel fuel that is intended to replace fossil fuels. Some UN scientists believe that these plantations could lead to the extinction of the species.

Logging

Vast areas of forest have been destroyed by the logging industry where the destruction of the trees is worsened by the construction of many roads built to aid the removal of the timber.

Forest fires

Forest fires have also caused many serious problems. Consequences of the logging and Palm oil industries are that they allow the moist forest to dry out and cause wildfires that in 1997-1998 devastated huge areas in Borneo. Similar fires raged in Sumatra in 2004 and in the same year the IUCN Red List estimated that there were just 7,334 Sumatran orangutans left. It is reported that fires still burn annually in both Sumatra and Borneo.

Drought

The most recent drought of 2006 in Kalimantan is thought to have killed several hundred orangutans in just six months, primarily because of forest loss due to resultant fires and to the conversion of forest to agriculture which resulted in loss of habitat and food shortages.

The Pet trade

Last but not least, poaching and the pet trade remain major threats to orangutans across most of Borneo and Sumatra. Several hundred have been confiscated and returned to orphanages where they are rehabilitated into the wild.

Outside protected areas

The majority of remnant wild populations of orangutans in both countries are located outside of protected areas, in forests that are exploited for timber production or in the process of being converted to agriculture.

> **Did you know? ...**
> Life span of orangutans in the wild is up to 40 years or more, but information is limited.

> **Did you know? ...**
> The Sumatran species is Critically Endangered and the Bornean species is Endangered according to the IUCN Red List of mammals, and both are listed on Appendix I of CITES.

Orangutan hand   *Orangutan foot*

Hand and foot of orangutan showing the similarity between these and human appendages. Note the small size of the thumb and big toe. The phalanges are long to aid climbing

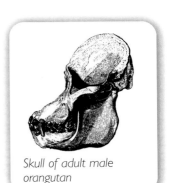

Skull of adult male orangutan

The Sumatran Orangutan
Pongo abelii

Status

The IUCN - The World Conservation Union classifies this Orang-utan as Critically Endangered (1976) and by the USDI (1980). and is on Appendix 1 of the CITES.

What's in a name

mpongi is a Congolese name originally used for the gorilla but now used for the orangutan. The Bornean orangutan's species name *pygmaeus* is from the Ancient Greek pugmaios meaning 'small, dwarfish' which is misleading since this animal is quite large. The name *abelii* is in honour of Dr Clark Abel, a British physician who lived for a few years in Sumatra in the early 19th century and described Orangutans.

Head of male Bornean Orangutan

Head of male Sumatran Orangutan

The Sumatran orangutan is almost exclusively arboreal in contrast to the Bornean orangutan, especially Bornean adult males, which more often descend to the ground. Female Sumatran orangutan rarely travel on the ground and adult males do so only when necessary. They are found in several types of forest, both at low altitude and in mountainous forest and also in coastal peat swamp forest.

Physical difference

Sumatran orangutans tend to be slimmer than Bornean orangutans, with longer faces, and, usually, the sparse, coarse, shaggy hair is longer and paler. Youngsters are bright orange.

Physical appearance

Besides being much larger than females, adult males have large cheek pads or flanges, but Sumatran males have smaller cheek pads than Bornean males. The males also have a large pouch on the throat, and they develop "beards" as they grow older. The pouch is used as an aid in vocalising when it is inflated. The throat pouch and cheek pads give the male face a huge fleshy appearance. This difference between male/female is called sexual dimorphism. The faces of both male and female adult orangutan are bare with dark skin.

Social habits

Adult male Sumatran orangutans spend most of their time alone. They are very territorial and hold large home ranges that they defend from other males, these may overlap the territories of several females. They announce their home ranges to attract females by making a series of grunts that echo and can be heard perhaps a half mile away; this call is probably amplified by the throat pouch and is called 'the long call'.

Female Sumatran orangutans will spend some time with other adult females, perhaps relatives, but they usually stay with just their infant or juvenile offspring.

> **Did you know? ...**
> *Sumatran orangutan prefer fruit, although they will also eat leaves, insects (such as termites and ants) and, on rare occasions, small mammals.*

Sexual maturity

Sumatran orangutan females become sexually mature between 7 to 10 years of age. There are long intervals between births for about 8 to 9 years. This compares with 6 to nearly 8 years for the Bornean orangutan. Gestation lasts for about eight months and the female nurses the single infant for about three and a half years. The young will start to eat solid foods after about four months and as the infant grows it becomes less and less dependent on its mother, but may not leave her care until it is at least six years old. Care of the youngster is undertaken exclusively by the mother

Habitat

Although both species depend on high-quality primary forests, Sumatran orangutan appear less able to tolerate habitat disturbance than the Bornean orangutan. They are also the most endangered. The IUCN Red List of Endangered Species states that there are only about 7.300 left in the wild, although a new population is being established in the Bukit Tigapuluh National Park, Jambi and Riau Provinces, via the re-introduction of confiscated illegal pets. This

Did you know? ...

The Sumatran Orangutan height for an adult male is 168.5 cm (5 ft 6 in). Weight for an adult male is up to 139.5 kg (308 lbs), with females weighing about half this. Arm length is 116.6 cm (3 ft 10 in) with a arm span of 233.7 cm (7 ft 8 in). Leg length is 76.8 cm (2 ft 6 in).

population currently numbers around 70 individuals and is reproducing, but numbers otherwise generally continue to drop.

Endangered

This species is seriously threatened by wholesale conversion of forest to agricultural land and palm oil plantations and both legal and illegal logging. Fragmentation by roads is also a threat that will be increased if the Ladia Galaska road network in Aceh Province, where most Sumatran orangutan live, is legitimised by the Indonesian government. This will rapidly fragment most of the populations within the Province. They are also illegally hunted and captured for the international pet trade but this appears to be because mother orangutan are killed as pests when they raid fruit crops at the forest edge. In parts of North Sumatra orangutan are also still hunted on occasions for food.

The Gunung Leuser National Park is the most vital habitat for the long-term survival of the Sumatran orangutan.

Habitat

The Sumatran Orangutan
Pongo abelii

Bornean Orangutan
Pongo pygmaeus

Status

The IUCN - The World Conservation Union classifies this Orang-utan as Endangered (2008) It is on Appendix 1 of the CITES.

What's in a name

The Congolese name *mpongi* was probably used originally for the gorilla but some time later it was used as Pongo to represent the orangutans.

Pongo pygmaeus pygmaeus is the Northwest Bornean orangutan. It ranges from northwest Kalimantan (Indonesia) to Sarawak (Malaysia).

The Greek *pygmaios* means: small, dwarfish, which is misleading because the orangutan is quite a large animal. It was probably used as a comparison to humans.

P. p. wurmbii is the Central Bornean orangutan that occurs in southwest Kalimantan and central Kalimantan.

Baron F. von Wurmb (1742-1781) described a (dead) specimen of this subspecies in 1784 in what was then southwestern Borneo.

P. p. morio is the North-eastern Bornean orangutan and can be found on East Kalimantan to Sabah (Malaysia).

Sir Richard Owen (1804-1892) was a comparative anatomist who named this orangutan *morio* in 1837 but without explanation. It is to him that we owe the Natural History Museum in South Kensington.

(Information Professor Colin Groves)

The Bornean Orangutan is more solitary than the Sumatran Orangutan. It is endemic to the island of Borneo where it is present in the two Malaysian states of Sabah and Sarawak, as well as in three of the four Indonesian Provinces of Kalimantan. Distribution is now highly patchy throughout the island and is apparently absent or uncommon in the south-east of the island, in central Sarawak, the Sultanate of Brunei and in western Sabah.

Flanged males

Like the Sumatran orangutan, the Bornean orangutan has two different forms of mature males: flanged and unflanged. This is called 'bimaturism'.

Flanged males have a facial pouch, flanges and a throat sac and, compared to the Sumatran species, their cheek pads are markedly larger and covered in short bristly hair.

Territorial males

They are very territorial and hold large home ranges that may overlap the home ranges of several females; they defend these ranges from other males, being rather intolerant and aggressive towards any other adult males that enter their home range.

Echoing calls

In a similar way to the Sumatran orangutan male, they announce these territories, to attract females by making a call that echoes through the forest and can be heard perhaps a half mile away, this call is amplified by the throat pouch and is called 'The long call.'

Unflanged males do not possess the secondary sexual characteristics: the facial disk, flanges and throat sac. They differ from the flanged, mature, males by a) being smaller and about the size of an adult female;

b) they do not emit 'Long calls' nor do they show intolerance to other males. However, both types of male can, and do, sire offspring. Unflanged males change to the flanged form when reaching maturity.

> ### Did you know? ...
> *Bornean males are slightly larger than Sumatran males; they average:*
> *Height: up to 1.7 m (5 ft 7 in)*
> *Weight: up to 120 kg (264.6 lb)*
> *Females are smaller: Height: 780 mm (2 ft 6.7 in), Weight: 37 kg (81.6 lb)*

The flanged, mature, male is much larger than the female and possesses a long coat of dark red hair.

Female maturity

Female Bornean orangutans reach maturity between 10 and 15 years old and reproduce every six to eight years on average.

Birth and infancy

Females generally give birth to a single infant after a gestation period of approximately eight and a half months. The female nurses the infant for about three and a half years. After about four months the young will start to eat solid foods but may not leave the female's care until it is at least seven years old. Care of the youngster is exclusively with the mother.

Males and females generally come together only to mate.

What do they eat?

The diet includes leaves, bark, flowers and insects. More than 500 plant species have been recorded in their diet, with fruits making up about two thirds of their average intake. Availability of fruit affects all aspects of their life:

their ranges, seasonal movements and general behaviour.

Habitat

Bornean orangutans prefer low-lying forests to upland areas. The low-lying flood-prone forests and peat swamps produce more regular and larger fruit crops than dryer upland forests and so have the highest orangutan densities.

Population numbers

The most recent estimates for Bornean orangutan numbers are between 35,000 and 69,000 individuals. These estimates were obtained between 2000 and 2003. Since recent trends are steeply down in most places due to logging, burning and palm oil farming it is possible that the current numbers are below these figures.

Habitat

BORNEO

Location map of the Bornean orangutan Pongo p. pygmaeus showing main conservation areas and National Parks in red and general habitat locations in orange..

The Northwest Bornean Orangutan
Pongo pygmaeus pygmaeus

43

Gibbons

Also called the lesser apes, gibbons differ from the other great apes, the chimpanzees, gorillas, orangutans and humans, in being smaller, in not making nests, and in certain anatomical details in which they superficially more closely resemble monkeys than great apes do, being relatively small, slender, and very agile.

Similarities and differences to other apes

There are fourteen species of gibbons which are classified according to their size, anatomy and vocalisations. They have many of the general characteristics of primates, e.g. flat faces, stereoscopic vision, enlarged brain size, grasping hands and feet, opposable digits and like other apes they have no tail and their arms are longer than their legs. Unlike other great apes they are not sexually

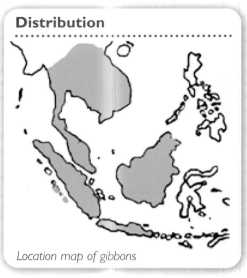

Distribution

Location map of gibbons

dimorphic in size, but mature females usually weigh more than mature males.

Brachiation and mobility

They use their arms, helped by the very long hands, fingers and short thumb, which together form a hook, to help in a spectacular swinging motion called brachiation.

They also have very good bipedal locomotion which they use on stable surfaces too large to grasp, or on rare occasions when on the ground, when their arms are held up to keep from dragging and to assist with balance. They can sometimes be seen putting their weight on their hands and swinging their legs through as if using crutches.

Distribution

They are native to the dwindling rain forests of southeast, south, and east Asia, where their natural habitat is being destroyed at an alarming rate. (More information about location will be shown for each individual species).

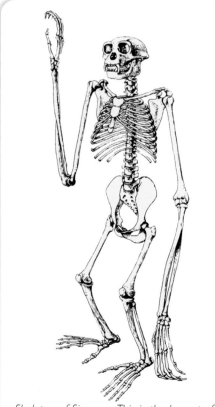

Skeleton of Siamang. This is the largest of the gibbon species. Note that the arms reach the ground when in the upright position even when the legs are straight. (After Schultz modified by Hutchins 2009)

> ***Did you know? ...***
> *Longevity of gibbons in the wild is 25 to 30 years but can be as long as 40 years in captivity.*

Family groups
They pair often for life with the adult female being the dominant animal in the group. The adult males subordinate to them. They live in small families composed of the mated pair and up to four offspring.

Reproduction
Full sexual maturity occurs at 5-7 years. The gestation period varies from 210-235 days. Weaning is gradual but occurs between 18 and 24 months.

   The young are physically independent at about three years, mature at about six, and usually leave the family group at about eight, though they may spend up to ten years in their family group.

Sleeping arrangements
Gibbons do not build nests like the great apes. They sleep sitting up with their arms wrapped around their knees and their head tucked into their lap.

Loud voices
Gibbons are renowned for their loud, complex calls that can be heard over long distances and are used to announce their location, defend territory, and to develop and maintain bonds between paired males and females.

   The song of the adult pair is composed of separate male and female elements to identify individuals. Each pair develops its own variation. The singing usually takes place at dawn to announce location and territory, but it may also be heard at other times of the day. However, these songs can make them an easy find for poachers.

Skull sizes

Skulls of adult gibbon in comparison to skull of man. (After Schultz modified by Hutchins 2009)

Hands and feet

Gibbons have developed the ability to progress underneath branches by swinging their long arms in a form of locomotion called brachiation. This primary mode of locomotion, brachiation, enables them to swing from branch to branch for distances of up to 15 m (50 ft), at speeds as high as 56 km/h (35 mph). They can also make leaps of up to 8 m (27 ft) but they do climb readily with all four limbs and walk on level ground and branches, with their arms raised for balance, either quadrupedally or bipedally. They are the fastest and most agile of all tree-dwelling, non-flying mammals.

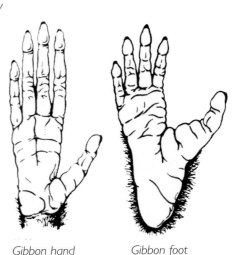

Gibbon hand   *Gibbon foot*

What do they eat?
Most gibbons are primarily frugivorous supplemented with insects, birds' eggs and small vertebrates, but this varies by species.

Conservation threats
All gibbons are endangered, largely due to deforestation. They are also hunted and trapped for the pet trade. All are Endangered or Critically Endangered depending upon species. It is known that Chinese medicine traditionally believes that gibbon bones provide effective treatment for rheumatism!

The Siamang
Symphalangus syndactylus

This is the largest of the gibbons and is native to the forests in the hills and mountains of peninsular Malaysia, and in the Barisan Mountains of Sumatra in Indonesia. Both male and female are always black with long shaggy fur, especially on the arms and legs.

Status

The IUCN - The World Conservation Union classifies the Siamang as Endangered (2008).

What's in a name

The Siamang is the only species in the genus *Symphalangus*. It has the first two fingers on each hand fused together, this gives the genus name *Symphalangus*, which is made up from the Ancient Greek *sym* meaning: together, and *phalanx*, with the genetive *phalangos*, meaning: soldiers in line of battle or, in this case, fingers or toes.

The species name "*syndactylus*", is made up from the Ancient Greek *syn*, meaning: "united" and *daktulos* meaning finger or toe. They differ from other gibbons in that they have the second and third toe webbed together.

Siamang is a Malay native name for the gibbon.

The Siamang, like other gibbons, are the top trapeze artists of the animal world. Using the brachiation mode of motion they can leap between branches to incredible distances from 30 to 50 feet. They will use their feet to carry objects while using their arms to move through the trees. Siamangs hold their arms above their heads for balance when walking bipedally, which they appear to do better than other gibbons.

Communication

The Siamang is distinctive also in having a large amplifying throat pouch called a "gular sac" which is found in both the male and female. This can be inflated to almost the size of their heads, allowing them to make loud resonating calls or songs that excels the vocalization of other gibbons.

The female using her vocal pouch, which she blows up like a balloon, starts to emit a series of barks alternated with booms, followed by a series of whoops and short barks. These gradually accelerate and finish with a very loud yell. Between each female call the male calls in a higher pitched scream, followed then by a combined "song" which rises in pitch to end with the very loud high-pitched boom of the male. It is a display to denote territory and location and can be heard for a great distance.

Did you know? ...

Height:, male and female; 73.7 to 88.9 cm (2 ft 5 in to 2ft 11 in). Weight: male 11.9 kg (26.2 lb) Female 10.7 kg (23.6 lb)

Mixing with other gibbons

Siamangs are the only gibbons to mix with other gibbon species and live within the combined ranges of the Agile Gibbon *Hylobates agilis* and the Lar Gibbon *Hylobates lar*.

Sleeping arrangements

All the gibbons have tough, horny pads on their buttocks known as ischial callosities and since they do not build sleeping nests, these pads help them to sleep comfortably, seated on tree branches and safe from predators.

Family grouping

Siamangs live in family groups led by a dominant male, and sometimes male offspring stay in the group untill well after maturity, helping to care for the younger siblings. They protect one another and are very sociable. They huddle together in groups of two or three when they sleep.

What do they eat?

Siamang diet includes: flowers, fruit, leaves, nuts and shoots of plants, supplemented by insects, small animals, birds and bird's eggs.

Birth and infancy

Sexual maturity is reached at about seven years of age. The gestation period is seven months after which a single offspring is born. The young are naked at birth and for the first few months, the baby clings to the mother's abdomen for comfort and warmth. The young are independent by the age of two but remain with the family.

Conservation threats

The illegal pet trade takes a toll on wild populations but the main threat is habitat loss in both Malaysia and Sumatra. There has been approximately 70-80% loss of primary Siamang habitat within the past 50 years. Palm oil production, the roads that service them and expanding agriculture are the problems that cause this.

The Siamang is now listed as Endangered by the IUCN. It is believed that the species has declined by at least 50% over the past 40 years.

There is some comfort in the fact that this species is one of the most adaptable gibbons to habitat change. According to the IUCN, although the species occurs in numerous protected areas and retains a number of viable populations, it could in future be considered Critically Endangered and should be closely monitored in the future.

Habitat

Location map of the Siamang Symphalangus syndactylus *showing general habitat locations in orange. Siamangs are found in some numbers in the Malay Peninsula and Sumatra.*

Above: Male and female of the Siamang, *Symphalangus syndactylus*

47

The Lar Gibbon
Hylobates lar

What's in a name

The genus name *Hylobates* is made up from the Ancient Greek *hulé* meaning: a wood, a forest; *bainō* meaning: I walk, I step; and *batës* meaning: one that treads or, a climber.

The species name lar comes from the Latin *Lar*, an ancient honorary title in Rome, equivalent to the English 'Lord'.

Lar gibbons range extensively in the evergreen tropical rain forests of South East Asia, and have the greatest north-south range of any of the gibbons.

Where they live

The species is found in Myanmar (Burma), Indonesia, Laos, Malaysia and Thailand. They are very rare in China and may in fact be extinct there, but if any still exist they would only be found in Southwest Yunnan in their former range. Moving south from China, Lar gibbons are found throughout most of Thailand, except in the north-east. The range extends east of the Salween River in southern and eastern Myanmar. They are found through the Malay Peninsula except for an area between the Perak and Muda Rivers near the Thai-Malay border. Lar gibbons are also found west of the Mekong River in northwestern Laos and in northern Sumatra.

Subspecies distribution

The distribution of the subspecies is as follows: *H. l. lar* are found in peninsular Malaysia and possibly Thailand.

H. l. carpenteri is found in eastern Burma, west Laos, and north Thailand. *H. l. entelloides* is found in southeast Myanmar and in central and south Thailand. These are coloured black or light buff with a white face ring, and white hands and feet; the white face ring is often fainter in the female.

H. l. vestitus is found over the northern third of the island of Sumatra, Indonesia, and are coloured brown to red or buff.

Did you know? ...
Lar, or white-handed gibbons live to 15 years in the wild, in captivity they have been known to have lived up to 50 years of age.

Did you know? ...
Male size 44-60 cm (1 ft 5 in to 2 ft 0 in) Male weight 5–7.6 kg (11 lb to 17 lb) Female 42–58 cm (1 ft 5 in to 1 ft 11 in). Female 4.4–6.8 kg (9.7 lb to 15 lb)

Sexual colour differences

Adults have a ring around the hairless face which is less apparent in lighter individuals, all have white feet and hands that contrast with the rest of the body, hence the common name of White-handed gibbon. Individuals have light and dark phases, with light individuals having buff or creamy pelage and dark individuals having brown or black pelage.

Locomotion

Lar gibbons are adapted for life in the trees and usually move through their environment using brachiation, but they can walk, bipedally, tripedally, or quadrupedally They hop, run, climb, swing and leap, bridging great distances.

What do they eat?

Lar gibbons eat a large variety of foods, especially fruit, including figs, (which often make up a large proportion of the diet); other fruits: liana fruit, tree fruit and berries but also new and young leaves, buds and flowers, vine shoots, insects including mantids and wasps and even birds' eggs. They drink water from tree holes by cupping their hands

Sexual maturity

Male Lar gibbons mature between 8 and 12 years. Females reach sexual maturity at between 8 to10 years and have one offspring every 3 to 5 years.

Birth and infancy

They have their first offspring at the age of about 9 years, after a gestation period of around 7 months. For the first two years of its life, an infant gibbon is carried everywhere by its mother. After weaning the baby gibbon moves around independently, but will follow its mother, closely, for up to 3 years. They may continue to live close to the borders of their parent's territory for several more years until settling into their own area with a mate. Often a strong male comes to live with a group (with a male, female and young) apparently quite without any problems, but he remains subordinate to the previous male.

Conservation threats

The major threat to this species is hunting for subsistence food and for the pet trade. Hunting pressure varies across the range, but takes place even within protected areas. Inadequate management and protection are important long-term threats and conservation efforts must increase to identify the hunters and educate them into the advantages of tourism. A further threat is road construction through protected areas, especially the north-south highway in Peninsular Malaysia. Road building poses a threat because it promotes forest clearance and strip development, causing fragmentation of rain forest and increased access to hunters. Much forest loss is due to slash-and-burn agriculture and the increasing commercial plantations of palm oil. In Sumatra, most of the lowland forests have been cut down to provide way for a network to link the west and east coasts of Aceh province. This means that much of the remaining forest is at risk. There are also many natural predators like big cats and raptors.

Male, right, and female of the Lar gibbon, *Hylobates lar (Buffy males and black females also occur).*

49

Kloss's Gibbon or Mentawai Gibbon
Hylobates klossii

What's in a name

Named after Cecil Boden Kloss (1877-1949) who was a zoologist living in Singapore during the years 1903 to 1932. He was director of the Raffles Museum in Singapore from 1923 to 1932.

Kloss's Gibbon or the Mentawai Gibbon is endemic to the Mentawai Islands, located off the west coast of Sumatra, Indonesia.

Both male and female Kloss's gibbons have short, dense, glossy, black hair from birth. They have a broad chest and the limbs are long.

The thumbs and big toes are also very long, and there is webbing between the digits of the hands and feet, similar to the Siamang. It resembles the Siamang with its black fur, but is considerably smaller and lacks the Siamang's distinctive throat pouch.

Habitat and locomotion

It is diurnal and inhabits the rain forest where it hangs in the trees from its long arms and rarely comes to the ground.

Bonding and territories

They pair usually for life, using social grooming to help to maintain bonds, and they claim a territory from approximately 20 to 30 hectares in size, which they defend strongly against other gibbons.

Family grouping

The reproductive cycle of Kloss's Gibbon is similar to that of other gibbons. As young males and females reach sexual maturity they will leave the family group and establish new groups. As they mature these groups consist of a breeding pair and their offspring, Males and females form monogamous pairs.

Reproduction

Every two to three years the female may give birth to a single young. The gestation period is seven to eight months The young are weaned in the middle of their second year, and gain maturity in about seven years.

> **Did you know? ...**
> The singing of Kloss's gibbon are considered the most beautiful of all the gibbons' songs – 'the purest note in nature', one musician called it.

Defence calls

Kloss's gibbon groups defend a territory with loud bouts of singing, serving to proclaim ownership to warn off other animals from their territory and possibly to strengthen the family bonds.

The beautiful song

The singing of Kloss's Gibbon is considered the most beautiful of all the gibbons' songs. Males and females will sing at considerable length, but not in duets unlike most other gibbons, particularly during the morning and evening; males chorus before dawn and females after dawn with a 50 second great call.

What do they eat?

They feed mainly on fruit, but will also take flowers and some invertebrates to supplement the diet, also eating different plant parts, birds' eggs, insects and small vertebrates.

> **Did you know? ...**
> Size: 44–63 cm (1 ft 5.3in to 2 ft 0 in)
> Weight 6 kg (13.23 lb)

Conservation threats
The main threat facing these gibbons is habitat destruction and degradation caused by human activity in the area, especially the destruction of the rain forest by the logging industry. Hunting for subsistence food and for the pet trade are also threats.

Life expectancy
The life expectancy of Kloss's gibbon is about 25 years in the wild, and up to 40 years in captivity.

Habitat

Kloss's gibbon occurs on the islands of North and South Pagai, Sipora and Siberut in the Mentawai group of islands, West Sumatra, Indonesia. The Mentawai Islands are situated 85 to 135 km off the coast of West Sumatra between 0°55' to 3°20' South and 98°31' to 100°40' East.

Male and female of Kloss's gibbon,
Hylobates klossii

The Agile Gibbon and Borneo White-bearded Gibbon
Hylobates agilis **and** *Hylobates albibarbis*

What's in a name

The Latin species name *agilis* means: Light, quick, nimble. The Latin name for the Bornean White-bearded gibbon, *albibarbis*, is made up from *albi*, meaning white and *barbis* meaning beard.

The Agile Gibbon inhabits the areas of Southeast Asia which include the south part of the island of Sumatra, the southwest of the island of Borneo and a small area on the Malay Peninsula.

Three subspecies

There are two subspecies of the Agile Gibbon:

Mountain Agile Gibbon, *Hylobates agilis agilis*, found in Sumatra and the highlands of South Peninsular Malaysia;

Lowland Agile Gibbon, *Hylobates agilis unko*, found in Sumatra and the lowlands of South Peninsular Malaysia.

Bornean White-bearded Gibbon, *Hylobates albibarbis*, found in Southwestern Borneo;

Most scientists list the Bornean White-bearded Gibbon *Hylobates agilis albibarbis* as a distinct species.

Locomotion

Their long arms enable them to swing from branch to branch very rapidly, where they can cover a distance of 10 metres from branch to branch, they hardly ever come to the ground. They prefer the upper rain forest canopy where it is difficult for predators, like snakes and raptors, to catch them.

Colour variations

The fur colouring of Agile gibbons can vary from black, or very dark brown, sometimes red-brown, to a pale phase which is buff to blonde, depending on the subspecies, but all subspecies have white brows. Males are easily recognised by their white or light-grey cheeks. The hands and feet are the same colour as the rest of the body but may be a little darker. The dark phase is mostly found in mainland South East Asia, but half of those found in Sumatra have the light colouring. Males are slightly larger than females. White-bearded gibbons are more parti-coloured than Agile gibbons.

Bonding and reproduction

Agile gibbon pairs are monogamous, but many do not mate for life. The

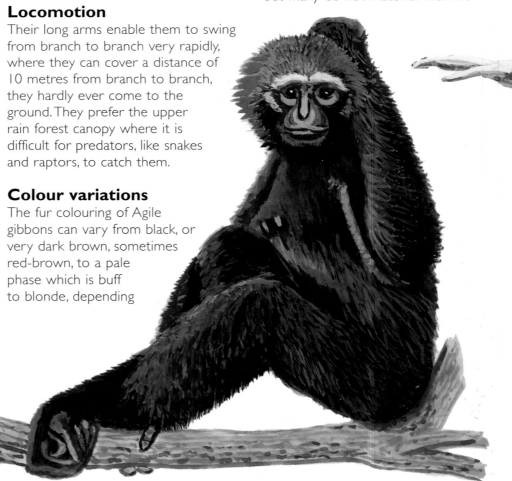

female gives birth to one young after a gestation period of seven months, and both male and female help with caring for the young. Pairs may reproduce up to a total of six young in their reproductive lifetime. The baby is weaned at about 2 years of age and becomes fully mature at about 8 years; it then leaves its family group in order to look for a mate.

Singing as defence

They live in a strictly guarded territory and can be heard singing duets early in the morning to defend and establish an area of about 20 to 30 hectares. When the singing is not enough, they are known to chase intruders away, but occasionally an intruding male or female ousts one of the established pair and takes its place.

What do they eat?

Diet, much like other gibbon species, consists of fruit, leaves, and flowers and is supplemented by birds' eggs and insects.

Conservation threats

As with all wildlife in South East Asia this species is threatened with extinction due to loss of habitat to massive deforestation for logging and agricultural development, but poaching for meat and the pet trade are a serious problem. However, parks and reserves have been established to preserve the species, and some Agile gibbons are bred in zoos.

Did you know?
In captivity, this species can live up to 44 years but may not live as long in the wild.

Female and male of the Agile gibbon, *Hylobates agilis* **Both black and buff males and females occur.**

Did you know? ...
Male size: 40–60 cm (1ft 3.7in to 2ft)
Male weight: 5.5 kg (12.13 lb)
Female size: 42–58 cm (1ft 4.2in to 1ft 10.8 in) Female weight: 4.4–6.8 kg (9.7–15 lb)

Habitat

Location map of the Agile gibbon and White-bearded gibbon showing general habitat locations.

The Pileated Gibbon
Hylobates pileatus

What's in a name

The genus name *Hylobates* is made up from the Ancient Greek *hulé* meaning: a wood, a forest; *bainō* meaning: I walk, I step; and *batës* meaning: one that treads or, a climber. The Latin species name *pileatus* means 'wearing a felt cap'.

Did you know? ...
Male size: 44–63.5 cm (1 ft 5.3 in to 2 ft 1 in)
Male weight: 7.7 to 10.4 kg (17 to 23lb)
Female weight: 6.3-8.6 kg (14-19 lb)

The Pileated gibbon inhabits the tropical rainforests of eastern Thailand, western Cambodia and southwest Laos west of the Mekong River.

They are found in evergreen rainforest including semi-deciduous monsoon forests, mixed deciduous and evergreen forests throughout their range.

Sexual dimorphism
Mature males have a purely black dense fur except for the light coloured hands and feet. There is a thick white eyebrow band that continues in a partial ring around the eyes; the crown hair is flattened towards the back of the head with whitish hairs over the ears. The genital area is also white. Females have a white-grey or greyish-buff coloured fur with only the belly and head black. They have a white, and often shaggy hair ring around the head.

Family grouping
Pileated gibbons are active during the day, spending rest periods and night's in tall trees. They live in small family groups which consist of a breeding pair and their offspring.

Bonded for life
It used to be thought that all gibbons mate for life, but now we know that sometimes one mate gets ousted and replaced – this happens in Siamangs and in Lar and Agile gibbons, but we don't yet know whether it happens in Pileated gibbons, or whether their pair bonds are stronger. The female is dominant, and like all other gibbon species, they reinforce bonds by social grooming.

Love songs
The bond between breeding pairs is reinforced through 'duets'. A male call is shorter than the female call. The female's song is typically made up of about seven to eight phrases of 'great calls' with a long dramatic 'wobble' at

Did you know? ...
The life expectancy of the Pileated gibbon in the wild is about 25 years but can be up to 34 years in captivity?

the end and the duration of these varies significantly between individuals from different localities.

Family groups
It is believed that these vocalizations are also necessary to establish and maintain the family groups' territory which they also defend with displays and threats.

Birth and infancy
Females give birth to a single infant every two or three years. The gestation period is 7 to 8 months. The young, especially females, tend to stay with the parents until they are ready to start their own family at between seven or eight years of age and females may even breed in their parents' group.

What do they eat?
The majority of their diet consists of fruits, including figs, but they also eat leaves, flowers, buds and insects, including spiders. They also eat other invertebrates, birds' eggs and small birds. Pileated gibbons drink water by immersing their hands into water or against wet leaves and then licking the water from their fur

Conservation threats
The main reasons for the decline of the Pileated gibbon include habitat loss, especially due to logging and agriculture, as well as hunting for food and the pet market.

**Female and male of
the Pileated gibbon,**
Hylobates pileatus

Habitat

*The Pileated
gibbon inhabits the tropical
rainforests of eastern
Thailand and western
Cambodia west of the
Mekong River.*

Müller's Bornean Gibbon
Hylobates muelleri

What's in a name
The genus name Hylobates is made up from the Ancient Greek *hulé* meaning: a wood, a forest; *bainō* meaning: I walk, I step; and *batēs* meaning: one that treads or, a climber. The species name *muelleri* means that this gibbon was named after Baron Sir Ferdinand Müller (1825-1896), an Australian botanist and explorer.

Müller's Bornean Gibbon is endemic to the island of Borneo where it inhabits the northern and eastern part of the island.

Subspecies
There are three subspecies of this gibbon:

Müller's Gray gibbon, *Hylobates muelleri muelleri* is found in southeast Kalimantan, Indonesia, approximately south of the Mahakam River and west of the Barito River.

Abbott's Grey Gibbon, *Hylobates muelleri abbotti* is found in Kalimantan, Indonesia and in Sarawak, Malaysia. It occurs north of the Kapuas River and as far east as the Saribas District of Sarawak.

Northern Grey Gibbon, *Hylobates muelleri funereus* is found in Brunei, Kalimantan, Indonesia and in Sabah, and Sarawak, Malaysia. It ranges from Sabah in the northeast of Borneo, south to the Mahakam River and perhaps west to the Baram District and the IV Division of Sarawak.

Habitat
It is found in semi-deciduous monsoon forests and tropical evergreen forests that are either of primary or secondary forest types. In the southwest of the island the Agile Gibbon lives and surprisingly their territories hardly overlap; but in areas where the Agile Müller's gibbons are sympatric, hybridisation between them has been observed.

Appearance
The colour of this gibbon ranges from grey to brown with a lighter ring of

Did you know? ...
Unlike other gibbon species, Müller's Bornean Gibbon does not show sexual dimorphism in its fur colouration, both male and female look alike.

Did you know? ...
Their life expectancy in the wild is similar to other gibbons at about 25 years but may be longer when in captivity.

hair surrounding the face. The hair on top of the head is darker than the body hair. Unlike many other gibbon species, Müller's Bornean Gibbon does not show sexual dimorphism in its fur colouration. It is one of the smaller of the gibbons.

The dominant female
They have a monogamous mating and social system which is reinforced by social grooming between individuals, but the female tends to be more dominant than the male.

Birth and infancy
The female produces a single young every two to three years, after a gestation period of seven months, and both male and female help with caring for the young. Pairs may reproduce up to a total of six young in their reproductive lifetime. The baby is weaned at about 2 years of age and becomes fully mature at about 8 years. It then leaves its family group in order to look for a mate.

Love songs
Vocalizations occur between the breeding male and female, and are dominated by the female who calls in short, rising notes and a short bubble, whereas the male gives single hoots. This singing is important because it helps to maintain the pair bond between the breeding pair and also it helps to establish and maintain the territory.

What do they eat?

Müller's gibbon is a fruit eater, it prefers to eat fruits high in sugar, including figs, but will also consume immature leaves, flowers, and insects. They drink by immersing their hands into water or against wet leaves and then licking the water from their fur.

Conservation threats

Though it is mostly revered, especially by the indigenous people, it is still probably hunted for food. Hunting pressure varies across the range, but takes place even within protected areas. Another threat comes from illegal trading in pets that takes a toll on wild populations and efforts must increase to identify the hunters and educate them into the advantages of tourism. The main threat is habitat loss caused by the construction of palm oil plantations, and the roads that service them. These intrusions promote forest clearance and strip development causing fragmentation of rain forest and increased access to hunters.

Expanding agriculture is also a serious problem where huge areas of forest habitat are cleared. Inadequate management and protection against forest destruction create long-term threats to conservation.

Habitat

Location map of Müller's Bornean gibbon

Male, left, and female of Müller's gibbon,
Hylobates muelleri

> *Did you know? ...*
> Size: 42-47 cm (1 ft 4.5 in to 1 ft 6.5 in)
> Weight: 5.7. kg (12.6 lb)
> Male and female of similar size and weight.

The Silvery or Moloch Gibbon
Hylobates moloch

What's in a name
The species name *moloch* was named by Jean Baptiste Audebert (1759-1800) who was a distinguished naturalist. He named this gibbon after Moloch, a Semitic god, to whom children were sacrificed but this latter probably has no significance.

The Silvery gibbon is endemic to Java and is mainly confined to the western provinces of Banten and West Java, but is also present in central Java as far east as the Dieng Mountains.

Subspecies
Some authorities believe that there are two subspecies of the Silvery Gibbon: **Western Silvery Gibbon** or Western Javan Gibbon, *Hylobates moloch moloch*. **Eastern Silvery Gibbon** or Central Javan Gibbon, *Hylobates moloch pongoalsoni*.

Habitat
Its habitat consists of undisturbed primary forest and montane forests with a rather dense and close canopy.

The Silvery gibbon appears to prefer the taller trees for resting, foraging and locomotion.

Distinctive colouring
Silvery gibbons, as their name suggests, are fluffy with greyish-white fur. The fur is very long and some gibbons have a dark silver-grey patch on the top of their round heads. Both males and females have the same colouring.

Very long arms
Their extremely long arms, like all gibbons, have a span at least twice their height to help them brachiate through the trees more easily.

Family grouping
Silvery gibbon families are very closely linked, and they stay close together when travelling. Adolescent gibbons will stay with the family until they mature and leave the group to find a mate.

Sexual maturity
Age of sexual maturity is about 8-10 years The age of first reproduction may be about 10-12 years, There is no breeding season and a female will come into oestrus at any time of the year.

Birth and infancy
Silvery Gibbons live in pairs, and the female will produce offspring about every two to three years. Pregnancies usually last seven to eight months, and only one offspring is born at a time. The young are born almost hairless with only a small tuft of hair on the top of their heads. There are 2-3 years between births.

Defence calls
They live in a strictly enforced territory of about 20 to 30 hectares which they protect with vigorous visual displays and songs. The female starts early in the morning with a haunting song that can be heard for long distances. The male is not so vocal. When the singing is not enough, they are known to chase intruders away, usually with a lot of noise and crashing through branches. Unlike most other gibbons they do not duet, only the Kloss gibbon, like the Silvery gibbon do not duet.

What do they eat?
Like other gibbons the majority of their diet consists of fruits, including figs, but they also eat leaves, flowers, buds, and insects. They also eat other invertebrates, birds' eggs, and small birds. They drink water by immersing their hands in water or against wet

Did you know? ...
Male size: 44–59 cm (1 ft 5.3 in to 1 ft 11 in) Male weight: 6 kg (13 lb) Males and females are very similar in appearance and size.

leaves and then licking the water from their fur. They move quietly through the canopy, the only sign that they are there is a moving branch or a piece of falling fruit.

Habitat loss

Silvery gibbons are under threat due to habitat destruction and fragmentation from illegal logging, the illegal pet trade and encroachment from local human populations. The gaps in the forest effectively limit the arboreal Silvery gibbon to restricted areas around mountain and volcano tops. Habitat disturbance is now relatively slow, and populations of gibbons, while isolated, seem to have become more or less stabilised in recent years.

Conservation efforts

A gibbon rescue and rehabilitation workshop was conducted in 1997 hosted by Conservation International and the University of Indonesia and it was agreed that a rescue and rehabilitation centre was needed and education programmes were proposed. The most viable protected population is found within the Guning Halimun National Park. The species has bred successfully in captivity in Indonesia and some are held in captivity outside their natural range.

> **Did you know? ...**
> The Silvery gibbon's life expectancy in the wild is similar to other gibbons at about 25 years but they may live longer in captivity.

Silvery gibbon
Hylobates moloch

Habitat

The Silvery gibbon is endemic to the western half of Java, Indonesia. Most populations can be found in the western province, but a few remain in central Java.

The Hoolock Gibbon
Hoolock hoolock and *Hoolock leuconedys*

The Hoolock gibbon is found south and east of the Brahmaputra River in Assam, India; Myanmar (Burma), Bangladesh and in south Yunnan, China. It is now considered a separate genus to the Hylobates gibbons.

Status

The IUCN - The World Conservation Union classifies the Hoolock gibbon as Vulnerable (2008) and they are listed under CITES Appendix I

What's in a name

The genus and species name *hoolock* derives from Hulluk the native Burmese name for the gibbon. *leuconedys* comes from the Greek *leukos* meaning white and *nedus* meaning groin.

Habitat

Location map of the Hoolock gibbon showing general habitat locations. The Hoolock gibbon is now found in north Myanmar (Burma), Assam, north east India and in south western Yunnan, China.

Where they live

Habitat is in tropical and monsoonal evergreen rainforest where preference is for the closed canopy of three-tiered forest vegetation, where trees in the higher tier support sleeping, resting and sun basking and the trees in the middle and low tiers provide locomotion paths and food.

Sexual colour differences

Hoolock gibbons exhibit sexual dichromatism: the adult male is always black, except for its prominent white eyebrows, the adult female is gold or buff or brownish buff. juveniles are coloured like adult males. There are two species,the Western *hoolock*, in which the white eyebrows are seperate, and the Eastern *hoolock*, in which they are joined. The Eastern hoolock also has a white tuft of hair in the groin. The Chindwin River in Burma seperates the two species.

Sleeping and resting

The Hoolock gibbon is arboreal and diurnal. It sleeps in a sitting posture, with its head buried between its knees, and during the hot hours of the day, it retires to lower, more shady trees and rests.

Locomotion

Like other gibbons the Hoolock gibbon moves either by brachiation when leaping or jumping between the trees, by bipedally walking on tree trunks or on the ground, or by acrobatic and climbing movements on vines and tree trunks. When walking on the ground, it usually holds its long arms upward or horizontal for balance

Family grouping

Hoolock gibbons live in small, monogamous family groups, consisting of a mated pair with their offspring. The size of a group ranges from 2 - 6 members. There are deep social bonds between group members. Mother-infant interactions are common.

These family groups maintain a definite territory. The area of these territories usually ranges between 15 - 35 hectares (38 - 88 acres) which they defend by loud and frequent territorial songs. Unlike *Symphalangus*, *Hylobates* and *Nomascus*, the songs of males and females are very much alike, being very harsh, aided by small throat sacs. There is sometimes aggression between groups which usually takes place in areas where the territories of two or more groups overlap.

Sexual maturity

Sexual maturity in both sexes is attained at approximately 7 years.

Birth and infancy

Mating occurs early in the rainy season, and, after a gestation period of between 195-210 days the infant is born. There is usually a single infant. The newly born infant always clings to the mother's belly when feeding on her milk, weaning starts in about 6 months. The mature newborn always shares the night bed with its mother until another baby is born. Time between births being, usually, 2-3 years. The mother-infant bond is very strong,

Did you know? ...

Head & body length:
60-90 cm (1 ft 11.6 in to 2 ft 11 in)
Weight: 6-8.5 kg (13.2lb to 18.7lb)

with the mother protecting the infant from other group members as well as predators.

What do they eat?

Like most other gibbons, the Hoolock gibbon is frugivorous. Fruit, mainly figs, comprises the majority of its diet, which also includes leaves, flowers, buds and a small amount of insects and spiders.

Conservation threats

The Hoolock gibbon has declined mainly due to habitat loss. It is currently threatened by continued fragmentation of the rainforest caused by slash and burn cultivation and logging. In addition, severe hunting pressure by local tribesmen is reported, especially in Assam and China where the meat and bones are valued for use in Oriental medicine. They are also caught as pets .

When their habitat is fragmented, the gibbons are forced to descend from trees to cross clearings where the forest has been destroyed, making them even more vulnerable to hunting and predation. Further danger occurs when they sometimes enter villages to plunder cultivated gardens. They have a dislike of large bodies of water although they can swim well.

Male, left, and female of the Western Hoolock gibbon, *Hylobates hoolock*

The Yellow or Buff-cheeked Crested Gibbon
Nomascus gabriellae

What's in a name

Gabrielle Maud Vassal (1880-1959), an Englishwoman, whose name this gibbon carries, lived in Nha Trang, Vietnam, with her husband, Joseph Marguerite Jean Vassal, (1867-1957), a scientist working at the Pasteur Institute of Nha Trang. They worked with the famous microbiologist Alexandre Yersing. Together they collected a number of important type specimens, including skins of the Yellow-cheeked gibbon, for the British Museum (Natural History); but it is recorded that it was Gabrielle Vassal herself who shot the specimens of this species.

The skins were sent to Michael Oldfield Thomas (1858-1929), the curator of mammals, at the British Museum (Natural History). He described this gibbon as *Hypobates gabriellie* in 1908. In his paper (Thomas, 1909), Oldfield Thomas writes:

"I propose to name it in honour of Mrs. Vassal, to whose help much of her husband's success in obtaining interesting animals has been due."

The genus name *Nomascus* is from the Greek, meaning 'I observe a sac which relates to the fact that there is a visible scrotum which is unlike *Hylobates* gibbons.

The Yellow-cheeked Crested gibbon occurs in southern Laos, southern Vietnam and eastern Cambodia

Habitat

It is found in tropical lowland evergreen forests. They appear to prefer the upper canopy where they sleep, sitting up and resting amongst the trees. Like other gibbons, it is an arboreal and a diurnal species.

An unstudied species

The Yellow-cheeked Crested gibbon remains virtually unstudied in the wild.

Sexual colour differences

There is sexual dichromatism in that the colouration of adult females strongly contrasts with that of adult males: females have a bright yellow or pale orange pelage, but also have a black patch on the top of their heads.

The pelage of adult males is black with small pale yellow or pale orange cheeks. Males also have a black crest on the top of their heads, thus the name "crested gibbon."

Birth and infancy

These gibbons give birth to a single offspring, with an interval between the births of about 2-3 years. The gestation period is about 7 months. The young gibbons are born with virtually hairless ventral parts and rely on their mother for warmth. Nursing lasts about two years.

Colour changes

The young gibbons of both sexes at birth have a bright yellow colour coat. This colour changes to black during the second half of the first year, with only the cheek patches remaining yellow.

> ### Did you know? ...
> Life span of the Yellow or Buff-cheeked Crested gibbon in captivity is up to 50 years

They then resemble adult males in their fur colouration. The females turn back to the yellow colouration when attaining sexual maturity, but retain a black patch on the top of their heads. The timing of the colour change varies and takes several months to complete.

Sexual maturity

Young gibbons will stay with their parents until they are past adolescence and they usually reach sexual maturity at about 6-8 years. At this age the young gibbons leave their natal group, or may be chased off by their parents to find mates in a different group and locality.

Family grouping

They live in small, monogamous family groups which probably consist of an adult pair with two to four offspring.

Each family group occupies an area of about 20-50 hectares, but the typical territory size of this species has not been reliably determined.

Social grooming plays an important role in reinforcing the bonds between group members.

Defence and mating calls

The territories are defended by loud morning songs and by actively chasing intruders off the territory. This singing probably serves not only to defend territories, but to claim and protect food trees, to seek partners, and also to help to attract potential mates. The Yellow-cheeked Crested Gibbon, like all gibbon species, has a unique song which is usually initiated by the male. Immature family members sing together with their mother. The male usually finishes the song after the female has stopped singing. Unlike *Symphalangus* and *Hylobates*, the male's song is more complex and more strident than the female's. These songs appear to be inherited and not learned.

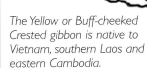

Habitat

The Yellow or Buff-cheeked Crested gibbon is native to Vietnam, southern Laos and eastern Cambodia.

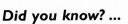

Did you know? ...
Male size: 60-80 cm (1 ft 11.6 in to 2 ft 7.5 in)
Male weight: 7-7.4 kg (15.4-16.3 lb)
Both sexes are of similar body size.

What do they eat?

It is mainly frugivorous, but they will also consume leaves and insects.

Conservation threats

The species is threatened by habitat loss from building development, logging and by hunting for food; they are also threatened because their body parts are used in Oriental medicine. The pet market also reduces populations. The species is still abundant in Cambodia.

The Yellow or Buff-cheeked Crested Gibbon,
Nomascus gabriellae

White-cheeked Crested Gibbon
Nomascus leucogenys and Nomascus siki

Status

The IUCN - The World Conservation Union classifies the Northern White-cheeked gibbon as Critically Endangered (2008) and they are listed under CITES Appendix I

What's in a name

The genus name *Nomascus* is from the Greek, meaning 'I observe a sac', this relates to the fact that there is a visible scrotum which is unlike the *Hylobates* gibbons. The species name *leucogenys* is made up from the Greek *leukons* meaning white and *genus* meaning the cheek.

The name *siki* is from an animal held as a pet by the famous ornithologist Jean Delacour and maybe derived from an African Boxer called 'The Battling Siki'.

Did you know? ...
Size male and female: 47-64 cm (1 ft 6.5 in to 2 ft 1 in)
Weight: Males 5.6 kg (12.3 lb)
Females 5.8 kg (12.8 lb)

White-cheeked Crested gibbons are found in Laos, Vietnam and southern China in evergreen tropical rainforests and monsoon forests.

Subspecies

The Northern White-cheeked Crested gibbon, *Nomascus leucogenys*, is native to northern Vietnam, Laos, and the Yunnan province of China. The Southern White-cheeked Crested gibbon, *Nomascus siki* is native to southern Vietnam and Laos; they were previously considered to be conspecific.

Physical differences

The male Northern White-cheeked Crested gibbon has longer hair and the white cheek patches are higher on its face than its northern cousin. The white cheek whiskers in the southern species extend round the mouth and under the chin. The female is a yellow colour and has dark brown to black patches on the top of the head. There is virtually no difference in colour between the females of either of these gibbons.

Family grouping

Like all gibbons, white-cheeked gibbons live in small monogamous families composed of a mated pair and up to four offspring. The adult female is dominant in the group

Birth and infancy

Females give birth to a single offspring every two or three years after a gestation period of seven months. The Infants cling to their mother from birth lying horizontally across the female's abdomen, allowing the mother to sit with her knees up, as

Did you know? ...
The average life span of the White-cheeked Crested gibbon in the wild is 28 years

most gibbons do. Youngsters are weaned early in their second year.

Colour changes

When born the infants are a beige colour, but by the time they are one and a half years old, their coat becomes black, with white cheek patches. At sexual maturity males remain black and females become a beige colour again.

Maturity

The young are physically independent at about three years and mature at about six years when they usually leave the family group, though they may spend up to ten years remaining with their family.

What do they eat?

White-cheeked Crested gibbons are frugivorous and spend most of their time in the forest canopy searching for leaves, flowers, leaf buds, shoots, and insects. There is some evidence that White-cheeked Crested gibbons are less frugivorous than other species of gibbons.

Defence and mating calls

As with other gibbon species they defend their range as their group territory. Defence takes the form of calls, starting with an introductory sequence when both male and female 'warm up;' this is followed by alternating sequences of male and female calls, then the female sings her 'great call'. The singing bout ends with a loud swooping call from the male. The calls are often accompanied by confrontations and chasing across boundaries, though there is rarely any physical contact between the males.

Conservation threats

Threats to these gibbons include: human settlement, agricultural production and commercial timber extraction. These cause fragmentation and degradation of the rainforest and seriously inhibit the natural movement of these animals.

Human population growth in both of the White-cheeked Crested gibbon's range is probably the worst threat to the problems of habitat destruction. In China and Vietnam where the range of the gibbons is already small the population is classified as highly endangered because of massive human population growth encroaching on their territory.

In Laos, the natural habitat is more abundant, but with no legal protection the gibbons are likely to fall prey to the same pressures as in China and Vietnam.

Male Southern White-cheeked Crested gibbon, *Nomascus siki.*

Habitat

The Northern White-cheeked Crested gibbon is native to northern Vietnam, China, Laos and southern Cambodia, shown in yellow. The Southern White-cheeked gibbon is located in central Vietnam and Laos between 15° 45' and 20° North, shown in red.

Male and female Northern White-cheeked Crested gibbon, *Nomascus leucogenys*

Black Crested Gibbon
Nomascus concolor

What's in a name

The genus name Nomascus is from the Greek, meaning 'I observe a sac', this relates to the fact that there is a visible scrotum which is unlike *Hylobates* gibbons. The Latin species name *concolor* means 'of the same colour'.

The Black Crested gibbon occurs in Yunnan Province in southwestern China and in northern Vietnam.

Habitat

Its habitat in Vietnam is in tropical evergreen broad-leaved forests and semi-deciduous monsoon forests; in China it is more likely restricted to broadleaved evergreen forests

Sexual dichromatism

Males and females are strikingly different in appearance. The male is almost completely black. The female pelage is a golden or buff colour with a black patch on the breast and a black crest on the head. The common name of this species comes from this tuft of longer fur on the crown of the head.

Family grouping

Black Crested gibbons live in small family groups of about 5 individuals, this average group number appears more than is usual in gibbon populations, and there are sometimes two females in the group, but only one male.

Sexual maturity

Sexual maturity in both sexes is attained at approximately 7 years. The time between births is usually, 2-3 years. Mating occurs early in the rainy season and after a gestation period of about 7 months the infant is born. There is usually a single infant. Weaning starts in about 6 months.

Bonding songs

The breeding pair make a variety of calls which are amplified with the aid of a throat sac below the chin; males and females engage in vigorous bouts of singing: males grunt, squeal and whistle and the females sing their 'great calls' which echo throughout the forest. It is believed that these 'duets' are essential in pair bond formation and reinforcement, but also serve to advertise the presence of the group within the territory.

What do they eat?

Unlike most gibbons Black Crested gibbons have a lower intake of fruits and flowers and feed preferentially on leaves, a similar diet to the Siamang.

In China, in the rainy season, ripe sugar-rich fruit such as figs are eaten but they also eat leaves, flowers, buds, and insects, during the dry season they prefer foraging for leaves.

Close to extinction

The Black Crested gibbon is one of the world's most endangered primates. They were once widespread in forests throughout southern China and northwestern Vietnam and into Laos; but now, the only area where black gibbon populations were reported to be healthy are in Yunnan Province, China; they may now be on the very brink of extinction.

Conservation threats

Deforestation caused by timber logging and to make way for agriculture, especially Palm Oil production, and building development is a main threat. This species has suffered a dramatic declines due principally to this habitat loss, but also as a result of hunting, for subsistence as well as the pet and "medicine" trades.

The fragmentation of their habitat causes groups to become separated from the remaining population and it

> ***Did you know? ...***
> *Male and female size: 45-64 cm (1 ft 5.7 in to 2 ft 1 in). Male weight: 5 to 7 kg (12.6 to 23 lb). Female weight: 6.3-8.6 kg (14 to 19 lb)*

Did you know? ...
Life expectancy of this gibbon in the wild is about 25 years.

is estimated that about 75% of the Black Crested gibbon's original habitat has already been lost.

Conservation efforts

However, there are ongoing protection programmes; the main one is protection from international trade by its listing on Appendix I of the Convention on International Trade in Endangered Species (CITES).

Fauna and Flora International (FFI) have been involved in community awareness programmes in the area and there is pressure to designate the last stronghold of the species, the Che Tao Forest, in Vietnam as a Gibbon Sanctuary. In China, the largest population occurs within the Wuliang Mountain National Reserve. It is vital that any remaining viable populations and habitats are protected or this previously successful ape is in grave danger of disappearing.

Habitat

The Black Crested gibbon inhabits the monsoon and deciduous forests of north western Vietnam and southern Yunnan (China).

Male and female of the Black Crested gibbon, *Nomascus concolor.*

Cao-vit Crested and Hainan Crested Gibbon
Nomascus nasutus and *Nomascus hainanus*

The Cao-vit Crested gibbon, *Nomascus nasutus*, together with the Hainan Crested gibbon, *Nomascus hainanus* are the rarest apes and amongst the most critically endangered mammals in the world.

What's in a name

The genus name Nomascus is from the Greek, meaning 'I observe a sac', this relates to the fact that there is a visible scrotum which is unlike *Hylobates* gibbons. The Latin species name *nasutus* means: large nose.

hainanus, simply means 'from Hainan' an island off the coast of southern China

The Tai ethnic group that live in the same area as the Cao-vit Crested gibbon gave its name Cao-vit as a reference to the sound of this gibbon's male song, its call.

(Information: Professor Colin Groves)

Distribtion
The Hainan Crested gibbon is restricted to the island of Hainan; the Cao-vit Crested gibbon occurs in northeast Vietnam and adjoining Guangxi Zhuang Autonomous Region, China. The distribution area of each species is restricted to one single block of forest.

Differences
The Hainan Crested gibbon and Cao-vit Crested gibbon differ in their hair colouration and territorial calls. These characteristics, in association with the newly discovered genetic differences, suggest that the Hainan Crested gibbon and Cao-vit Crested gibbon be considered distinct species.

Colour variations
Adult male Hainan gibbons are entirely black but adult male Cao-vit Crested gibbons may have a slight tinge of brown on the chest.

Adult female Hainan Crested gibbons are yellow to beige-brown with a black cap; female Cao-vit Crested gibbons are of similar colour but the black cap may extend down the back, the ventrum is darker brown and the face is surrounded by a broad ring of light hairs. The hair grows outwards on the side of the face and in a more downward direction as it gets closer to the chin.

Family grouping
These gibbons lives in small family groups of between 4 and 8 individuals with either a monogamous male, a female, and their offspring or a male with two breeding females. The home range is from 100 to 500 ha with an average of about 360 ha.

Did you know? ...
*Male and female size for both species:
47-64 cm (1 ft 6.5 in to 2 ft 1.2 in)
Weight 7-9 kg (15.4 lb to 19.8 lb)*

Defence songs
Crested gibbons sing to defend territories and to attract mates.

Sexual maturity
Sexual maturity in both sexes is attained at approximately 7 years. The time between births is 2-3 years. Mating occurs early in the rainy season and, after a gestation period of about 7 months, the single infant is born. Weaning starts in about 6 months. It is not possible to distinguish the sex of young Crested gibbons because immature individuals do not differ in fur colouring or calls, and their sexual organs resemble each other

What do they eat?
Preferred food is fruit such as figs, but they also eat leaves, flowers, buds, and insects.

Conservation threats
Forest clearance and harvesting of resin in the adjacent pine plantations has caused shrinking habitats. Poaching is another cause of the problem. Further problems are that, in the Bawangling Nature Reserve, the most difficult time for the gibbons to find food is between February and April, when only seven of 40 known food-plant species are available. Also, because of the small size of the population, there are instances of inbreeding.

Close to extinction

The Cao-vit gibbon was thought to be extinct in southwestern provinces of China in the 1950s and 1960s, and was also feared extinct in Vietnam, but just 26 individuals were found in 2002 in China. In November 2004, 37 individuals were located in Vietnam. These numbers have dropped.

In the 1950s there were estimates of about 2,000 Hainan gibbons on the island of Hainan. This number had reduced to 21 by 1989, and to only 17 in 2007. There are considered to be only 11 left now.

There may be surviving individuals or groups not yet accounted for in the Diaoluoshan and Yinggelin Nature Reserves, both in Hainan Province in China.

Conservation efforts

The Bawangling National Nature Reserve in southwestern Hainan Island, China is believed to be the last and only refuge in the world for the Hainan gibbon. Captive breeding is not an option because at present there are no captive individuals. Attempts to capture any of the few wild gibbons has not been successful and would harm the viability of the remaining stock.

Habitat

■ *The remaining areas of known populations of the Cao-vit and Hainan Crested gibbons.*

□ *Former areas of known populations of the Cao-vit and Hainan Crested gibbons.*

Did you know? ...

In 2002 there were less than 70 known individuals of the Cao-vit gibbon. This number has dropped considerably. There are only around 11 Hainan Crested gibbons left living on the island of Hainan, China. It is the rarest ape in the world with the Cao-vit Crested gibbon the second rarest.

Female and male of the Hainan Crested gibbon, *Nomascus hainanus.*

Those who care

Gorillas and chimpanzees

Dr. Louis Leakey

The anthropologist and archaeologist, famous for his study of human origins, established the Institute of Primate Research in 1960 and was responsible for initiating Jane Goodall's decades-long field study of chimpanzees in the wild, and the similar projects of Dian Fossey, for gorillas, and Birute Galdikas, for orang-utans. Each went on to become world-renowned scholars in the field of primatology.

Dr. Jane Goodall, DBE

Began studying the Kasakela chimpanzee community in Gombe Stream National Park, Tanzania in 1960. In 1977 she established the Jane Goodall Institute (JGI) which

Bangha compares feet with Ian Henderson, Lefini Sanctuary Manager.

supports the Gombe research and is a global leader in the effort to protect chimpanzees and their habitats. In 1991 she introduced 'Roots & Shoots', a youth driven education programme, which currently has over 10,000 groups in over 100 countries, working on local and global community service projects.

Dr, Goodall continues her conservation efforts by giving lectures, worldwide, and spends as many as three hundred days a year traveling, which does not allow her to spend much time in Africa anymore.

Dr. Dian Fossey

Founded her "Digit Fund", named after her favourite gorilla, Digit, in 1978 to preserve and protect the world's last Mountain gorillas. Digit was killed by poachers in 1977 and so Dian Fossey took up the fight against the poachers. For this she was murdered in 1985.

The Dian Fossey Gorilla Fund International (DFGFI)

In 1992 The Digit Fund was renamed The Dian Fossey Gorilla Fund International (DFGFI) in memory of her commitment to gorilla protection and research. DFGFI also operates the Karisoke Research Centre in Rwanda, and maintains a staff of scientists, trackers and anti-poaching patrols in the Volcanoes National Park.

Collaboration

Forty years after Dian Fossey and Jane Goodall began their pioneering work with great apes, the two organizations that they founded have formed a partnership working together in the eastern Democratic Republic of Congo (DRC) that has significant gorilla and chimpanzee populations.

A conservation philosophy

In their separate spheres, both the Dian Fossey Gorilla Fund International (DFGFI) and the Jane Goodall Institute (JGI) have developed the same conservation philosophy that 'effective conservation must begin with the needs and priorities of local communities'.

Lesio-Louna and Lefini Reserves

The Lesio-Louna and Lefini Reserves are situated near Brazzaville in the Republic of Congo. The Lefini Reserve was created in 1951 and the Lesio-Louna Reserve was created in 1993; both were created as a sanctuary for the reintroduction of gorillas orphaned by the illegal bushmeat trade. They were upgraded to a Nature Reserve in 1999. They are currently managed through a joint partnership project between UK-based charity The Aspinall Foundation and the Government of Congo. The project employs over twenty patrol staff trained in anti-poaching and monitoring techniques.

Feeding orphan gorillas in reintroduction programme, Lesio-Louna, Congo PhotoIanRedmond.co.uk

A resued baby chimpanzee. These are lucky to have been found and cared for. Photographs courtesy of Karl Amman

The U.S. Fish and Wildlife Service

From its Division of International Conservation, Great Ape Conservation Fund awarded 63 new grants for field projects to support ten African countries and seven Asian countries. Grants were awarded for: effective deterrents to the killing of great apes and other wildlife; to monitor the illegal wildlife trade and other activities detrimental to ape survival and provide a model for similar efforts throughout west and central Africa; for Research and Conservation of Great Apes;

Those who care

Keeper shares water with Bangha a young gorilla at Lefini Gorilla Sanctuary, Congo.

to maintaining a constant field presence and community awareness; to secure the long-term survival of the Cross River gorilla population by enhancing community management activities and supporting a biomonitoring programme; protection of wild chimpanzees in three high priority classified forests in Cote d'Ivoire, in partnership with Wild Chimpanzee Foundation; to survey two classified forests and use the results to produce new management plans in collaboration with the national forestry agency and timber companies to improve protection of orangutans and gibbons and other wildlife and many other project grants throughout primate ranges.

Dr. Jo Thompson
First visited the Democratic Republic of Congo (DRC), (then called Zaire) in 1991 to carry out fieldwork for her doctorate. She has dedicated herself to helping the bonobo, its environment and the local human inhabitants and conducting biological field research, community-based conservation and wildlife education in the DRC.

Lukuru Wildlife Research Project
In 1992 she established the Lukuru Wildlife Research Project (LWRP), a territory of almost 24,000 square kilometres in the middle of the huge Congo rain forest.

In 1998, she bought 34 square kilometres of virgin terrain in the southern half of the LWRP and created the Bososandja Faunal Reserve.

She has helped many people in the DRC to understand the value of bonobos. The project's success is because of her frequent presence in the region and the fact that she 'goes in alone', without other foreigners. She works closely with her team of 20 local co-workers in the field, where, in her words she: "lives like they live, eating what they eat".

She has also raised huge sums of money in support of the bonobo.

The Cameroon Wildlife Aid Fund
CWAF was established in 1996 as a UK charity and its primary objective was to improve living conditions for primates housed at Mvog Betsi Zoo in Yaounde, Cameroon. Since then CWAF has expanded its mission significantly to provide sanctuary for wild orphans of the illegal bushmeat and pet trades in Cameroon and to work closely with the local population to protect their natural heritage through education and social support.

Orangutans

Dr. Biruté M. F. Galdikas
Dr. Galdikas gained her master's degree in 1969, during which time she met Dr. Louis Leakey. It took three years of persuasion to convince Dr. Leakey that he should consider her desire to study orangutans.

Camp Leakey
After he relented, in 1971, she arrived at the Tanjung Puting Reserve in Indonesian Borneo together with her husband the photographer Rod Brindamour. It was a wild place with no external means of communication, no roads, no electricity and no regular mail service. However, by the end of that year she had established Camp Leakey, named after her benefactor.

In 1975 she wrote the cover article, illustrated with Brindamour's photographs, for National Geographic magazine which gave the orangutan widespread international public attention for the first time.

The Orangutan Foundation International
In 1986, together with her doctoral student, Dr. Gary Shapiro, she set up Orangutan Foundation International (OFI), based in Los Angeles, California, with a presence in Australia, Indonesia, and the United Kingdom.

In recognition of her achievements, Dr. Galdikas has received many awards. The OFI carries out research, education, rehabilitation, world awareness and reintroduction of captured orangutans.

Cause to worry
In an alarming statement Dr. Galdikas said: "Unless extreme action is taken

Captured orangutan 'Roland' and friend, saved by the Orangutan Foundation. Photograph courtesy of The Orangutan Foundation

soon these forests could be gone within the next five to 10 years and wild orangutans along with them." Dr. Galdikas has conducted the longest continuous study, by one principal investigator, of any wild mammal in the world.

The Great Orangutan Project

The concept of this project is to combine the efforts of many partners to tackle the root causes of orangutan decline. The entire Great Orangutan Project is run by Way Out Experiences (WOX), with other partners which have a lot of input, amongst them are: The Sarawak Forestry Corporation (SFC), Zoo Negara, Zoo Taiping, and Batang Ai National Park local community including local tour

operators and government officials. Volunteers and sponsors also contribute to the long-term vision of thriving orangutan populations in Borneo.

Aims of the project:

This project shares a common vision 'to channel efforts towards a common goal and provide a forum for discussion and debate, education, research, improved public knowledge, and greater media involvement which can be achieved with the help, understanding and support of the global community.'

The Orangutan Foundation UK

Ashley Leiman OBE founded this organisation in 1990. Her involvement in conservation began over 20 years ago. She is one of the leading figures in orangutan conservation, having made numerous radio and television

appearances and published a number of scientific papers. She spends up to a third of the year in the field (most usually Indonesian Borneo) where she has in-depth knowledge and passion for this region.

The Orangutan Foundation is the world's foremost orangutan conservation organisation. The Foundation does much work in protecting the orangutans' tropical forest habitat, working with local communities and promoting research and education.

The Orangutan Foundation goes beyond that of purely protecting the orangutan. Critically it also includes a recognition that orangutan habitat is unique in its richness of biodiversity and crucial for local communities, who are as dependant on the forest as is the orangutan.

Sumatran Orangutan Conservation Programme (SOCP)

Is a collaborative programme involving the Indonesian Government's Department of Forest Protection and Nature Conservation, the PanEco Foundation, Yayasan Ekosistem Lestari (Foundation for a Sustainable Ecosystem) and the Frankfurt Zoological Society.

It is a diverse programme tackling all aspects of orangutan conservation including the confiscation, quarantine and re-introduction of illegal ex-pet orangutans; habitat conservation and protection; surveys and monitoring of wild orangutan populations; conservation education and raising awareness.

The SOCP also carries out field research into conservation and ecology of wild orangutans.

The SOCP maintains quarantine centres and reintroduction sites and is

Those who care

also developing conservation management strategies in forest and peat swamp areas on the West coast of Aceh. In addition, there are permanent long-term research projects at the Ketambe and Suaq Balimbing research stations, both in Aceh Province and education mobile units that continuously visit

This baby orangutan was once kept as a pet, but was successfully reintroduced back into the wild. Photograph courtesy of Perth Zoo, Australia.

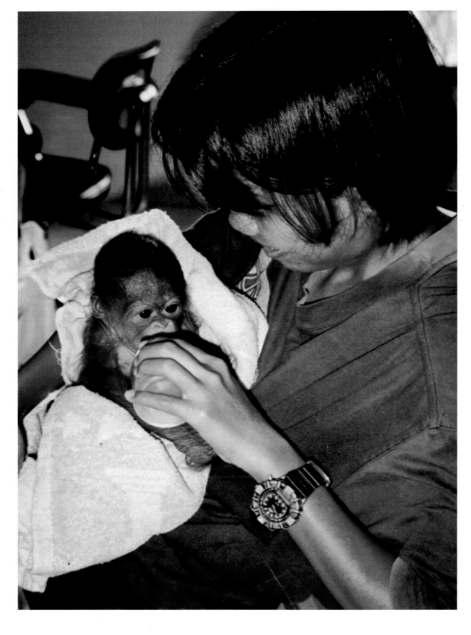

communities, schools and government departments in areas adjoining remaining orangutan habitat.

North American zoos no longer take orangutans from the wild, thus all new animals are captive-born.

Care for the captives
The Center for Great Apes' (CGA) provides a permanent sanctuary for orangutans and chimpanzees who have been

retired from the entertainment industry, from research, or who are no longer wanted as pets.

Patti Ragan
The CGA has roots in the rainforests of Borneo, where over twenty years ago in 1984, founder Patti Ragan spent several months volunteering at a rehabilitation project for wild orangutans. While there, her duties included tracking wild orangutans to observe behaviour for a long-term study project, and providing foster care for a group of infant orangutans. With her concern for orangutans (and chimpanzees) kept captive for medical research, circuses, and unwanted Sumatran/Bornean crossed animals she started the CGA in Florida, USA.

It is a nonprofit organization which provides care with dignity in a safe, healthy, and enriching environment for great apes in need of lifetime care.

Gibbons

The Bawangling Reserve, China
Only 15 individual Hainan gibbons were known to exist in this reserve in 2000 and that population may have now been reduced.

Since the end of 2001, a research and conservation programme on the Hainan gibbon has been undertaken by the Zoological Society of Paris, in collaboration with the East China Normal University and the Muséum National d'Histoire Naturelle.

The project intends to raise funds for the reinforcement of monitoring gibbon groups by the staff of the Reserve and to specify the population structure of the gibbons' small population. Also to map out the fragmentation of the habitat, in order to propose connections between patches of suitable habitat for the expansion of the population. A programme of involvement and education of local minorities is also planned.

The Gibbon Conservation Alliance

Is based in Zurich, Switzerland and was formed to help gibbon conservation.

Dr Thomas Geissmann gave a presentation at the Anthropolical Institute of Zurich University where he told of the imminent extinction of several gibbon species and on lack of public awareness about these threats.

As a result of this presentation, several students of the Anthropological Institute decided to help gibbon conservation by creating the Gibbon Conservation Alliance, together with Thomas Geissmann.

Projects include:

Promotion of gibbon conservation and research on biology.
Raising funds for these goals.

Public work: Increasing public awareness of the gibbons, increasing the accessibility of research results and increasing the awareness of the urgency of gibbon protection measures. This is done through publications, lectures, websites, CD's, exhibitions and so on.

Kalaweit gibbons and Siamang conservation programme Is dedicated to the protection of gibbon species in Indonesia. Kalaweit runs centres in Borneo and Sumatra for the Agile gibbon and the Müller's gibbon.

General groups

The Great Apes Survival Partnership (GRASP)

Is an innovative and ambitious project of the United Nations Environment Programme (UNEP) and the United Nations Educational, Scientific and Cultural Organization (UNESCO) with an immediate challenge - to lift the threat of imminent extinction faced by gorillas (*Gorilla beringei*, *G. gorilla*), chimpanzees (*Pan troglodytes*), bonobos (*Pan paniscus*) and orangutans (*Pongo abelii*, *P. pygmaeus*) across their ranges in equatorial Africa and south-east Asia.

More

The GRASP Patrons are respected individuals who have made outstanding contributions in the field of conservation. They use their position to advance the objectives of GRASP. The current GRASP Patrons are;
Dr. Russ Mittermeier, the Director of Conservation International
Dr. Jane Goodall DBE, the celebrated chimpanzee expert
Prof. Toshisada Nishida, Japan's globally-renowned primatologist
Dr. Richard Leakey, the celebrated Kenyan authority on wildlife conservation and world renowned paleontologist
Prof. Richard Wrangham, Professor of Anthropology, Harvard University
All have provided their world-renowned expertise and reputation to bring further attention to the plight facing the great apes.

Ian Redmond OBE

Is a tropical field biologist and conservationist renowned for his work with great apes and elephants. For more than 30 years he has been associated with Mountain gorillas through research, filming, tourism and conservation work.

As with his mentor, the late Dr. Dian Fossey, the main focus of his work shifted from research to conservation work after poachers killed Digit in 1978.

Digit was a young silverback in one of the Karisoke study groups who was killed so that the poachers could sell his skull and hands. On finding the headless, handless body of this gorilla, that Ian regarded as a friend, was a turning point in his life.

He established and chairs the Ape Alliance (70 organisations linked via www.4apes.com), and is now Chief Consultant for GRASP - the UNEP/ UNESCO Great Apes Survival Project, which he helped launch in 2001.

Orangutans being released back into the wild in the Lamandau River Wildlife Reserve, Central Kalimantan, Indonesian Borneo.

Those who care

The World Wildlife Fund (WWF)
Was formed in 1961 by noted biologist and African wildlife enthusiast Sir Julian Huxley, IUCN vice president Sir Peter Scott and director-general of the British Nature Conservancy E. M. Nicholson, amongst others.

Its mission is the conservation of nature, using the best available scientific knowledge to preserve the diversity and abundance of life on Earth and the health of ecological systems by protecting natural areas and wild populations of plants and animals, including endangered species;

To promote sustainable use of renewable natural resources; and promote the reduction of pollution.

Congo Basin
An area covering 126 million acres (51 million hectares) or more than a third of the Congo Basin forests has been zoned for conservation management, which includes the population of mountain gorillas in Virunga, between the Democratic Republic of Congo, Rwanda and Uganda,

The International Union for Conservation of Nature (IUCN)
Was founded in 1948 as the world's first global environmental organization. It is now the largest professional global conservation network. and a leading authority on the environment and sustainable development.

What does IUCN do?
IUCN develops and supports conservation science, particularly in species, ecosystems, biodiversity, and the impact these have on human projects around the world and supports governments and communities to develop conservation practice.

IUCN helps implement laws to protect wildlife and habitats and provides resources for training people and monitoring results.

Orangutans leaving the rehabilitation centre to be returned to the wild. Photographs courtesy of the Orangutan Foundation

Addresses of major Ape Conservation groups

IUCN/SSC Primate Specialist Group
John M. Aguiar, Coordinator
Conservation International
2011 Crystal Drive, Suite 500
Arlington, Virginia 22202-3787
Phone: (703) 341-2400 USA
www.primate-sg.org

The Dian Fossey Gorilla Fund UK
110 Gloucester Avenue,
London NW1 8JA
Tel: 0171-483 2681 Fax: 0171-483 4541 (International: 44-171-483 2681)
Reg. Charity No: 801160

WWF-International (UK)
Web (en): www.wwf.org
WWF-UK
Panda House, Catteshall Lane,
Godalming, Surrey, GU7 1XR
Phone: +44 (0)1483 426444
www.wwf.org.uk

Great Apes Survival Project (GRASP)
GRASP - UNEP/UNESCO
Great Ape Survival Project
c/o RSPCA Building, Lansdown,
STROUD, Glos. GL5 1BG,
Email: grasp@unep.org
www.unep.org/grasp/

Jane Goodall Institute
4245 North Fairfax Drive, Suite 600, Arlington, VA 22203
Phone: +(703) 682-9220
Fax: +(703) 682-9312
www.janegoodall.org

Zoological Society of London
Regents Park, London, NW1 4RY
Phone: +44 (0)20 7449 6610
www.zsl.org

Primate Society of Great Britain
Bramley Lane Farm, Higher
Kinnerton, Chester, CH4 9AX, UK
Phone: +44(0) 1334 467174
www.psgb.org

Lukuru Wildlife Research Project
Dr Jo Thompson
c/o P O Box 5064, Snowmass
Village, Colorado, USA

Primate Taxon Advisory Group
PO Box 20, Mosman NSW
2088, Australia
www.arazpa.org.au/primate_t.html

Animal Defenders International
Millbank Tower, Millbank, London
SW1P 4QP
Phone: +44 (0)20 7630 3340
www.ad-international.org

Bushmeat Crisis Task Force
Heather Eves
c/o The Wildlife Conservation
Society, 2300 Southern Boulevard,
Bronx, New York 10460
718-220-5100
www.bushmeat.org

Bonobo Conservation Initiative
2701 Connecticut Ave, NW
#702, Washington DC 20008,
USA
80 Avenue Nguma, Ma
Campagne, Kinshasa
Phone: 202 332 1014
www.bonobo.org

Bushmeat Project
Dr. Anthony Rose
Biosynergy Institute
P O Box 3430 Palos Verdes
California 90274, USA

Canadian Ape Alliance
c/o University of Toronto Joint
Centre for Bioethics
88 College Street,
Toronto, ON M5G 1L4,
Canada
www.great-apes.com/

Conservation International
2011 Crystal Drive, Suite 500
Arlington, VA 22202, USA
Phone: (703) 341-2400 USA
www.conservation.org

Great Ape Project
714 North 97th Street
Seattle, WA 98103
Phone: 206-579-5975
www.greatapeproject.org

Great Ape Trust of Iowa
Dr Benjamin Beck
4200S.E. 44th Avenue
Des Moines, Iowa 50320
Phone: +515 243 3580
Fax: +515 243 8997
www.GreatApeTrust.org

Humane Society of Canada
409-120 Carlton St, Toronto ON
M5A 4K2, Canada
Phone: +416 368 0405/1948
www.humanesociety.com

Humane Society US
2100 L Street,
NW Washington DC 20037
www.hsus.org

International Fund for Animal Welfare
87-90 Albert Embankment,
London, SE1 7UD
Phone: +44 (0)20 7587 6700
www.ifaw.org

International Primate Protection League (U.K.)
Gilmore House, 166 Gilmore
Road, London SE13 5AE
Phone: +44 (0)20 8297 2129
www.ippl-uk.org

International Ranger Federation
Gordon Miller
Fold Head Cottage, Grindsbrook
Booth, Edale, Hope Valley,
Derbyshire, S33 7ZD, UK
Phone: 00 44(0) 1433 670210
www.int-ranger.net

World Society for the Protection of Animals
89 Albert Embankment, London
SE1 7TP, United Kingdom
Phone: +44 (0)20 7587 5000
www.wspa.org.uk

Restore UK
PO Box 310, Epsom, Surrey, UK
Phone: 01737 355458
Fax: 01737 355496
www.restoreuk.org

Wildlifeline
Tammy Marlar
3rd Floor, Queens House, 1
Leicester Pl, London WC2H 7BP
Phone: 0845 130 6170
www.wildlifeline.org

Les Amis des Animaux au Congo
Claudine André
bonoboducongo.free.fr
Email: bonoboducongo@free.fr

Rettet den Regenwald e.V. (Rainforest Rescue)
Friedhofsweg 28, 22337 Hamburg
Phone: +49 40 4103804
www.regenwald.org

Lola ya Bonobo
Claudine Andre
10 avenue de l'Eglise, Ma
Campagne, Ngaliema, Kinshasa
Democratic Republic of Congo
Phone: +243 99 07 737
www.friendsofbonobos.org

WAZA Project Nr. 04014, operated by the Zoological Society of Paris in collaboration with the East China Normal University and the Muséum National d'Histoire Naturelle, Paris. The project is supported by Apenheul Primate Park, CERZA Lisieux, the zoos of Doué-la-Fontaine, Mulhouse and Thoiry, the Friends of Mulhouse Zoo, CEPA (Conservation des Espèces et des Populations Animales), ZGAP (Zoologische Gesellschaft für Arten-und Populationsschutz), Zodiac Nature Watch and the Gibbon Conservation Center.

Office Rwandais de Tourisme et de Parcs Nationaux (ORTPN)
Email: ortpn@rwanda1.com
www.ortpn.gov.rw
www.rwandatourism.com

Support for African/Asian Great Apes
Phone: 81-568-63-0547
www.saga-jp.org

Institut Congolais pour la Conservation de la Nature (ICCN)
Email: iccn@ic.cd
www.iccnrdc.cd

Uganda Wildlife Authority (UWA)
Ugandauwa@infocom.co.ug
www.uwa.or.ug

Primate Conservation INC
Primate Conservation, Inc is a volunteer non profit foundation dedicated to studying, preserving, maintaining and conserving the habitats of the most endangered primates in the world. Over 100 species, approaching half of all primates, are marked endangered. The tropical forests in Africa and Asia where most primates live are disappearing at an alarming rate.
www.primate.org

Mountain Gorilla Conservation Fund
Mountain Gorilla Conservation Fund exists to achieve the primary goal of saving gorillas from extinction. The Current Projects section of their website gives a brief description of eight of these projects. The Mountain Gorilla Conservation Fund is dedicated to ensuring the future of the Mountain Gorillas of Rwanda, Uganda and the DRC Congo. By providing a partnership of business, wildlife conservation, and community development, MGCF addresses the single biggest challenge facing preservation of these animals today; how do we help communities in developing areas grow and prosper without destroying precious habitat or the Mountain Gorillas, who call it home.
www.mountaingorillaconservationfund.org/

Scientific Names explained

The origin of Scientific names is credited to the Swedish naturalist, Carl Linnæus (1707-1778). He established the present system of scientific nomenclature, called the Binomial or Binominal classification, with the custom of making an animal's name consist of two, sometimes three, terms. The first indicates the name of the genus to which the animal belongs, the second is the name of the species and, sometimes, there is a third for the name of a subspecies.

Genus: is the class that includes various kinds of animals all of which possess in common certain essential characteristics. The generic term is always a noun.

Species: each of the kinds of animals included within a genus is called a species, which in its turn has certain characteristics that mark it off from all other species. These are usually adjectives but can sometimes be nouns either in apposition or in the genitive. The first letter is always written in lower case. The genitive is particularly used to record some person connected with the discovery of a species or sub-species when it is usually indicated by the two-syllabled termination, -ii, which represents the Latin genitive.

Subspecies: most species have themselves been divided into subspecies which are no more than variations whose basis is mainly geographical. This also is always started with a lower case letter.

In many names the same term occurs twice and in some names three times. When the specific (species) term is the same as the generic (genus) one this implies that the species in question is the typical species of that genus. Thus *Gorilla gorilla* which is the scientific name for the Western Lowland gorilla implies that this is a form of the typical species of the genus *Gorilla*. Also, in the case of the Western Lowland gorilla, in its scientific name *Gorilla gorilla gorilla*, the sub-specific term is the same as the specific one, this implies that the subspecies in question is the typical subspecies of that species.

The general acceptance by the scientific world of the Linnæan system brought two improvements to the naming of animals. Firstly, for international purposes, a single list of names replaced the various conflicting names that had been adopted by each separate country so that henceforth the same name denoted the same animal to every zoologist/biologist throughout the world. Secondly, the names that came into general use were simple and concise unlike the cumbersome references that they superseded.

The Roman man of letters, Pliny, wrote a Natural History and within Book X of this work, although devoted to birds, is our greatest source of ancient Latin names. The Greek philosopher Aristotle (384-322 BC) was president of the Lyceum which is regarded as 'The University of Athens'. Among the many works that he produced there was one entitled 'History of Animals' which contains many references that still survive. Other medieval and modern authorities to whom reference is made in the scientific and common names will be explained in the blue boxes, individually.

Bibliography

Haltenorth, T. & Diller.H.1984.
A Field Guide to the Mammals of Africa
William Collins Sons & Co Ltd.

Dixson, A.F. PhD. 1981.
The Natural History of the Gorilla
Weidenfeld and Nicolson.

Francis, C.M. 2008.
A field Guide to the Mammals of South-East Asia
New Holland Publishers (UK) Ltd.

Payne, J. & Francis, M. 1985
A Field Guide to the Mammals of Borneo
The Sabah Society with World Wildlife Fund Malaysia.

Gotch, A. F. 1979.
Mammals - Their Latin names explained.
Blandford Press.

Walker, E.P. 1984.
Walker's Mammals of the World, 4th Edition, Vol 1.
The John Hopkins University Press.

Macdonald, D. 1984.
The Encyclopaedia of Mammals, Vol 1
George Allen & Unwin.

Grzimek, B. 1990.
Grzimek's Encyclopedia, Mammals, Vol 2
McGraw-Hill Publishing Company.

Goodall, J. 1990.
Through a Window.
Weidenfeld and Nicolson.

van Lawick-Goodall, H & J. 1971
In the Shadow of Man
William Collins Sons & Co.Ltd.

DeVore, I. (Editor).1965.
Primate Behaviour, Field Studies of Monkeys and Apes.
Holt, Rinehart and Winston, Inc.

Matthews, L. H. 1969.
The Life of Mammals, Vols 1 & 2.
Weidenfeld and Nicolson.

Burton, M 1962.
Systematic Dictionary of Mammals of the World.
Museum Press Limited.

Napier, J. & Barnicot, N. A. 1963.
The Primates.
The Zoological Society of London.

National Geographic 1992.
Magazine - Apes and Humans
National Geographic Society.

Wilson, D. E. & Reeder, D. M. 1993.
Mammal Species of the World, A Taxonomic and Geographic Reference, Second Edition
Smithsonian Institution.

Caldecott, J. & Miles, L.
World Atlas of Great Apes and Their Conservation.
University of California Press.

Allaby, M. 2009.
Oxford Dictionary of Zoology.
Oxford University Press.

Index of English and Scientific species names